Yitzchak, Son of Abraham

He felt the presence of the Lord.

YITZCHAK
SON of ABRAHAM

by Zev Paamoni

*

Illustrated by John G. Harries

SHULSINGER BROTHERS

NEW YORK

Printed in Israel 1970

Set and composed at the Levanda Press Ltd.
Printed by Dfus Offset Israeli Leyetzu Ltd.

ILLUSTRATIONS

Chapter I

Names mean something. We're used to names like Bill, Joe, Clara, Sue, and Charlie. To us, they're just sounds that call to mind the faces of our friends and relatives. The names don't mean anything now; but they did when they were first invented. You could look it up.

We smile when we read about Indians named Sitting Bull or Rain-in-the-Face. Chinese names like Lotus Blossom and Golden Bells sound far-off and exotic.

So, too, in the prayers of the Jewish people "Our Fathers, Abraham, Isaac and Jacob" are sometimes run together as one word. The names don't mean anything. But they do!

Take the second name: Isaac. Mean anything? Not the way it's written. But in the beautiful language of the ancient Hebrews (and the modern Israelis) the name is pronounced "Yitzchak". It means "he will laugh".

That was the name they gave to the baby that was born to Abraham and Sarah in their old age. It was a good name and a true one. All of his life

— a life filled with excitement and adventure, pain and sorrow — Yitzchak remained cheerful and steadfast. He laughed.

Yitzchak was born in troubled times. The Cities of the Plain, Sodom and Gomorrah, had just been wiped out. By the Lord, because of their wickedness, people said. There was war — and peace — and more war.

All that passed over the head of the handsome little boy, with his dark curly hair flying and his white teeth flashing in his brown face as he ran between the tents of his father's encampment playing — at war. As he grew older, nothing pleased him more than to sit listening to his father as they sat in front of the tent while the burning sun set and the evening became pleasantly cool.

"The idols that the peoples of the world worship are not gods," Abraham explained. "They are statues of stone and wood. Our God is a spirit. He made the world and He can destroy it."

"**Will** He destroy the world," asked Yitzchak, wide-eyed, "the way He destroyed Sodom and Gomorrah?"

"Wickedness angers Him," said Abraham, sadly. "And when He is angry, He speaks with the voice of thunder and strikes with the strength of the lightning."

8

"He frightens me," said little Yitzchak.

"You do well to fear Him," said Abraham. "But goodness pleases Him; and when He is pleased, He blesses His children. The sun shines, the gentle rain falls. Crops grow tall and bread is plentiful. The sheep grow fat and there is meat to eat and wool to wear. If we are good—God is good."

"I will be good," promised Yitzchak.

Abraham laughed.

"Not because you fear God, but because you love Him. God is great and powerful, yet merciful. He loves His children. Even as I love you, my son, though I had to do what I did when you tried to spear my best ram yesterday."

Yitzchak looked at his father. Abraham's face was stern, but his eyes twinkled. Yitzchak laughed.

"He wasn't a ram," Yitzchak explained. "He was a huge horse pulling an Egyptian chariot. I had to kill him to stop the Egyptians."

"You try killing any more of my rams, my fine warrior," said Abraham, "and you'll run all the way to Egypt with me after you !"

Father and son looked at each other. Abraham smiled and Yitzchak laughed and laughed. They were wonderful evenings in front of the tent. Yitzchak never forgot them.

Abraham decided to settle down with his family. He chose a place midway between the Dead Sea and the Mediterranean Ocean. Egypt was far away to the south across the desert and Jerusalem far to the north, parallel to where the Jordan River empties into the Dead Sea.

Abraham dug a well. All the men worked. Yitzchak dragged buckets of sand and earth, while the sweat ran into his eyes. The women and girls brought food and water to the men at work.

The well was finally finished. Cool, clear water was drawn up and everyone drank. Yitzchak impatiently waited his turn. When he finished drinking, he said in surprise, "How much better the water tastes from the well I have dug!"

He joined in the general laugh that went up and they all went off to their tents to eat and sleep.

The next morning, when they tried to go to their well, they found the way barred by armed men. The local people claimed that the well was theirs and would not let Abraham or his family near it. They had many men with spears and bows and knives. That has always been a most convincing argument.

Yitzchak had all he could do to hold back the angry tears.

"That's our well. We dug it. What are we going

to do? Shall we attack them? Father, what are we going to do ?"

"We are going to dig another well," said Abraham quietly.

Six wells were dug. Each time the well was either taken away or filled in. Yitzchak's small body wasn't big enough to hold all his anger.

"Kill them, father, kill them," he would cry each time. "Why doesn't our God kill them? God doesn't like wickedness! Isn't it wicked to take away what someone has worked for? Why doesn't God kill them?"

"Don't ever question the ways of God," Abraham said quietly, "I never have. And I never will."

"What will you do, father?"

"You will see, my son."

The next day, Abraham called on the local chieftan, Abimelech. Abimelech stood tall and proud, with Phichol, the captain of his army, standing scornfully by his side. Yitzchak watched and listened.

The meeting began with polite words of welcome. Soon, however, the arguments became heated. Voices were raised in anger. Yitzchak watched his father fearfully. Not once did Abraham lose his calm.

"They'll kill him," thought Yitzchak. "They'll kill my father. Oh, where is God?"

When the shouting died down, Abraham spoke quietly, forcefully. He proposed that he pay for the next well that he would dig. He would give so many sheep and oxen. And seven lambs, one for each well.

"I agree," said Abimelech. "But one thing more. I see that your God is great and powerful, because everything you do turns out well. I want such a God on my side. Swear that you will help me against my enemies and I will swear that I will help you against your enemies."

"I will swear," said Abraham.

Abraham returned to his tents. A very quiet Yitzchak walked with him, holding his hand.

"What shall we do now, father?"

"Tomorrow we shall begin digging the seventh well. And then we start planting trees."

And so a city was born—Beer Sheba, the City of the Seven Wells.

CHAPTER II

Yitzchak grew up with the city, Beer Sheba — little by little, day by day. His father and the members of his little tribe built houses to live in instead of the tents they had been used to.

As each house was finished, another family moved from its tent into the new house. Each time, the family gave a feast for the other members of the tribe. There was food and drink. Songs were sung and dances danced. There was laughter and there was thanks and praise given to the one true God of the tribe of Abraham.

It was after one of these housewarming parties, late at night, that Yitzchak came home so tired that he was practically walking in his sleep. He was still happily humming one of the songs that had been sung at the party, but it was a good thing that his father had hold of his right hand and his mother had hold of his left hand. Little Yitzchak was so sleepy, he might not have gotten home otherwise.

No sooner had the family gotten home, when Yitzchak tumbled onto the pile of skins he used for a bed and fell fast asleep.

"Our son," Sarah whispered to Abraham, "Our handsome son. He is getting to be more like you every day, my husband. He, too, will be a great leader of his people."

"That will be as God wills," said Abraham.

Suddenly Abraham's face was intent and withdrawn. His eyes looked straight ahead as though they saw things no one else could see. Sarah knew that look.

Abraham walked out of the house, beyond the compound walls and over the sand dunes.

He walked steadily across the sand until he felt the presence of the Lord. He stopped.

"Abraham, tomorrow you will go to the Land of Moriah."

"Yes, my Lord."

"You will go to the top of the mountain and build me an altar."

"Yes, my Lord."

"There you will make a burnt offering to me."

"Yes, my Lord."

"You will take your son, your only son, Yitzchak, whom you love."

"Yes, my Lord."

"You will place him upon the altar and he shall be the burnt offering."

"Yes, my Lord."

"Do you understand, Abraham?"

"Yes, my Lord."

"Do you have any questions?"

"No, my Lord. Your command is clear."

"Then carry it out, Abraham."

14

Deep in thought, Abraham reached his home. He went in quietly and went straight to the bedside of his sleeping son. He gazed at him for a long time in the dim light.

Abraham turned away and went to his bed. Sarah woke.

"Abraham, my husband, what is the matter ?"

"Tomorrow, I am going on a journey. I am taking Yitzchak with me."

"But Abraham," Sarah objected, "Yitzchak is so young and the road is so dangerous these days. Are you going far?"

"To the Land of Moriah."

Sarah sat up.

"But that's a three day journey at the very least! Must you take Yitzchak?"

"The Lord's command must be obeyed," said Abraham. "We start at sunrise."

Chapter III

Yitzchak opened his eyes when the sun rose; then he closed them again. Lord, he was a tired boy this morning. He yawned widely and continued lying in bed with his eyes closed.

Usually, he jumped out of bed as soon as he woke up. This morning, though, he was tired. Besides, he had a lot to remember about the party last night.

It had been quite a party and Yitzchak went over it again in his mind, enjoying every detail all over again. First, the getting ready for the party and putting on new, clean clothes, a long shirt of sparkling white and a head cloth just like a big man's —only smaller. His sandals were new, too; but so small, so small.

Never mind. Some day he would be grown up. His beard would be full and long—like his father's. His step would be slow and dignified and he would stop and listen politely when people asked him questions and he would answer their questions in a loud voice, full of authority.

Last night, though, Yitzchak remembered smiling that he had had no patience to walk slowly. No one asked him any questions except his mother, Sarah, who asked him why he didn't stop fidgeting and sit and wait quietly like a good boy.

No, no. Yitzchak wanted to be a good boy; but he couldn't sit and wait patiently when there was a party to go to and his parents took so long to get dressed. He remembered finally running out of the house by himself to where the feast was in preparation and standing and watching.

He was not alone. There were other little boys and girls standing and watching the preparations. Most of them were his cousins. Almost every one in the tribe was related and these children were his first, second or third cousins.

His little cousins, too, were in their party finery; but some of the boys had been wrestling and rolling about in the sand. Their mothers would be very angry with them, thought Yitzchak with a smile. He would try not to get his new clothes messed or torn. He would just stand here quietly and watch.

When his cousin, Chesed, came over and pushed him, though—well, he couldn't just have stood there, could he? He just had to show him a trick or two he had learned about wrestling and, when Chesed said he had had enough, both boys got up laughing and brushing the sand off their clothes.

Yitzchak had hoped that his mother would not notice that his new white shirt had gotten a little torn in the scuffle. When Abraham and Sarah finally did arrive at the party, Sarah noticed the torn shirt first thing. She didn't say anything, though. She just looked at her son and shook her head.

Yitzchak breathed a little sigh of relief and set about having a good time at the feast. There were uncles and aunts to greet soberly and politely. There were cousins to grin at and whisper with. There were heavenly smells of roasting lamb and spices and palm branches. There was the mounting excitement and anticipation.

Then the great bonfire was lit in the courtyard and everyone took their seats around it. Abraham and Sarah were given the most honored place, of course. Wasn't Abraham the leader of the tribe? Yitzchak's chest swelled with pride.

"My father," he thought, "my father is the greatest and wisest man in the world. Of all the people in the world, God chose my father."

Yitzchak felt so good, he wanted to laugh, but he held back his laughter. People might ask him why he was laughing — and how could he tell them. So he kept quiet and listened to the singing.

The singing started slowly. Sad songs about lost

"Mother, he's letting me go along with him!"

"Come down here, you laughing hyenas, I'll give you something to laugh about."

lambs and about love. Then faster and more exciting songs about hunting and war. Everyone clapped hands and swayed in rhythm. Then the young men got up and danced. They stamped and shouted and leaped high in the air. Some of the bravest and the strongest of the young men leaped over the fire completely.

Only the men danced. The women sat modestly in the background. Yitzchak could harly keep still. He, too, wanted to stamp and shout and leap high in the air. But he knew that he would be frowned upon if he tried to dance. He was not yet a member of the tribe.

Three more years! Perhaps only two more years. Then he would be allowed to go through the manly rites of initiation. What a proud day that would be! He would be a man and a full member of the tribe. What glory!

Being a member of the tribe meant not only dancing around the fire at feasts and celebrations. He would be expected to defend the tribe with spear in hand, if the need arose. He would be expected to help his fellow tribesmen and every member of the tribe would help him if called upon.

Yitzchak stood straight and proud. For the moment, he did not hear the singing and the clapping. He did not see the dancers leaping and whirling. His eyes were looking into the future. He would not be an ordinary member of the tribe. No! He was Yitzchak, son of Abraham.

Abraham was the leader of the tribe; and one day Yitzchak, his son, would take his place as leader. Yitzchak was a little afraid. It was such a great responsibility. If the leader was strong and wise, the tribe prospered and increased. If the leader was weak and foolish, he could lead the tribe to disaster.

Yitzchak drew a deep breath, then another. He would not be afraid! He was not afraid! God loved Abraham. He had promised to make him father of a great nation. God would love Abraham's son, too, and cause him to lead wisely.

Yitzchak laughed, but no one heard him. There was so much noise and merrymaking going on. No, no one had heard him laugh; but Yitzchak, looking up, saw his father watching him. He had the feeling that his father knew what he was thinking about, knew why he had laughed. He felt ashamed and had hidden in the crowd of children.

The dancers tired and the singing stopped. Then the meat and drink were served. The roast lamb was delicious. Chesed and some of his cousins had managed to get hold of some wine and gave him a sip. Yitzchak's mouth burned and his head felt funny; but he asked for more—because men drank wine.

After the food had been finished, a hymn of thanksgiving and praise was begun; then another, and another. Then everyone grew quiet and looked expectantly at Abraham. Abraham rose to speak.

"My friends and kinsmen," began Abraham in his deep, serious voice. "We have celebrated tonight the raising of our dear brother's house. It is good to rejoice at a kinsman's good frtune and we are glad to be able to do so.

"But let us not forget to whom we owe our good fortune. Remember always the one, true Gd. In happiness, give thanks to Him. In sorrow, ask His forgiveness and seek his help. He will hear your voice. The Lord loves His children.

"I have lived a long time, but if I lived as many years again, I would not forget how the Lord God first appeared to me and said to me, 'Leave your country, your birthplace, your father's house and go to the land that I shall show you.'

"I did as the Lord commanded. I have always done as the Lord commanded. I shall continue to obey the one, true God as long as there is breath in my body. And the Lord has dealt well with me.

"My tribe increases and prospers. Our flocks

grow fat and we are not lacking in gold and silver. We live well and securely in the land the Lord promised to me.

"So, love the Lord, my brothers. Obey the Lord in all things. And we shall grow to be a great nation and a blessing to all the people of the world. These are the Lord's words. Remember them."

Abraham sat down. In respectful silence, each of the tribesmen and his family went up to their leader and bowed to him and took their leave. Until all had gone and Abraham and Sarah, with Yitzchak between them, went home.

Yitzchak opened his eyes and jumped out of his bed. He looked joyously at the bright morning.

"What a wonderful father I have," he thought. "I am so proud to be his son. Oh, it's good to be alive!"

Chapter IV

Yitzchak woke and ran out of the house and sniffed at the morning. The day was new and fresh. The rolling hills to the east glinted beautifully under the rising sun.

24

"A glorious new morning," thought Yitzchak and laughed joyfully. "Yes, it's good to be alive!"

Off he ran, as he did every morning to see how his friends, the lambs, were doing. They baaed their good mornings at him. The lambs knew Yitzchak and loved him and their mothers, the soft-eyed sheep, trusted him. The rams watched him as he walked among the lambs petting and examining them. No, this boy was a friend not an enemy. There was nothing to fear.

Yitzchak threw back his head and sniffed the air. There was a smell of breakfast cooking. He ran all the way from the sheep pens to the house. There was no hurry, but he ran because it felt good to run, just for the sheer joy of running.

Yitzchak went up to his mother and stood before her waiting to be noticed. When he caught Sarah's eye he said, "Good morning, mother."

"Good morning, son," said Sarah, kissing him. 'Did you sleep well?"

"Very well, mother; and you?"

"God be praised," said Sarah and then turned quickly "Reumah, you silly girl, what do you think you're doing?" The girl had spilt some water from the big pot onto the fire.

"Wait," said Sarah severely, "I'll help you. You

little idiot, don't ever try lifting that big pot full of water onto the fire by yourself."

"Yitzchak, my son," Abraham said.

"Yes, father."

"I am going on a journey, my son."

"Oh, where?"

"To the Land of Moriah."

"What a wonderful journey! I wish I could go, too."

"You a r e coming with me, Yitzchak, my son."

"Thank you, father," he said, when he could finally speak. "I shall try to be a help to you on the journey. I shall try not to make you ashamed of me or sorry that you took me along."

Abraham did not answer. Yitzchak thought he seemed sad. But, surely, that was impossible. How could anyone be sad if they were about to set off on an exciting journey that was bound to be full of adventure? No, no, father could not be sad, just thoughtful, perhaps. He must have many things to think about. There must be many preparations for such a journey. Good Lord! Preparations! Here he was standing and dreaming like a ninny when he ought to be helping his father prepare for the journey. And after boasting to his father about what a help he would be! Yitzchak felt ashamed.

"My father," he said, "What shall I do to help in the preparation for our journey?"

"There is no need, my son," said Abraham quietly, "Peleg and Naor are coming with us. They are making all the preparations now."

Peleg and Naor coming along on the journey! That was very good news. They were both jolly, brawny, brave lads. Peleg was an excellent wrestler. He had taught Yitzchak many tricks. Naor was strong as a bull. Stronger! And he never minded how much Yitzchak pestered him. He always had a joke ready that would make a boy laugh.

Oh, this was going to be a wonderful journey!

"When do we start, father?" he asked eagerly.

"Now," replied Abraham. "As soon as you've eaten. Go and eat your breakfast, my son."

"Yes, father," smiled Yitzchak, "I shall eat quickly."

He ran up to his mother.

"Mother," he said, "father is going on a journey."

"Yes", said Sarah, "I know."

"And, mother, he's letting me go along with him!"

Sarah did not answer. She suddenly turned

around and hugged her son closely to her. Yitzchak was indignant.

"Mother, stop it. I'm not a child!"

"No, Yitzchak," Sarah smiled through her tears, "you're not a child. You're my big son."

"Then stop worrying about me, mother. Nothing will happen to me."

Chapter V

Yitzchak crammed the last of the bread into his mouth and washed it down with the remaining goat's milk in the clay cup. He was on his feet and running while still swallowing and he pretended not to hear his mother calling him back.

Once outside the compound walls, he looked about for Peleg and Naor. There they were, farther off near one of the small outbuildings, putting a very large load on a very small donkey.

Yitzchak streaked after them and when he reached them, he did not stop but launched himself through the air and leaped upon Peleg's back. He threw a hammer lock around Peleg's neck and squeezed as hard as he could.

"Now I've got you, Peleg the champion wrestler,"

Yitzchak gritted through clenched teeth, "You can't get out of this hold. Do you give up ? Give up ?"

Peleg grunted, shifted, and heaved. Yitzchak went flying through the air and found himself lying on his back on a sand dune. Naor turned and looked at him with mock solemnity.

"What a lazy, little chieftan he is, to be sure," drawled Naor. "Just look at him — sleeping in the middle of the day. Don't bother waking him, Peleg. Well go off on the journey and leave him here sleeping."

Yitzchak jumped up and brushed the sand off, laughing.

"Some day I'm going to be able to throw you, Peleg," he said.

"Keep trying, little chief," said Peleg placidly, "You get better all the time."

"In a few years," Naor drawled teasingly, "Peleg will be an old man. Then it will be easy to throw him, little chieftan. Just be patient. It won't be long, now."

"I'll live long enough to make the funeral oration at your graveside, you tub of fat," said Peleg calmly.

"And a very fine oration it will be, I'm sure," said Naor, his black eyes twinkling. "Too bad you won't have any teeth left by then and nobody will be able to understand what you're saying."

Yitzchak laughed until his belly ached. Peleg and Naor were such fun to be with. What a fine pair of travelling companions they would make. Travelling companions! Lord, all this skylarking had made him forget why he had come running out here. The journey!

Yitzchak lent a hand while the two heaved the large load up off the ground and settled it comfortably on the donkey's back. Then he stood off and watched Peleg and Naor tie the load fast.

"Peleg. Naor. Do you know where we're journeying to?"

Naor turned and gazed solemnly at Yitzchak with his big, round eyes.

"Little chieftan," he said, "We are humble folk. Nobody tells us anything. Do you know where we are journeying to?"

"Of course I know," he said loftily. "We are journeying to the Land of Moriah."

"Thank you, little chieftan," said Naor soberfaced. "It is kind of you to inform your humble servitors. You know so much."

Yitzchak's chest swelled with pride. Still, he tried to preserve a modest demeanor.

30

'No, no," he disclaimed. "It's just that my father takes me into his confidence sometimes."

"How fortunate for us that you consider us your friends," said Naor, bowing low, "Or perhaps I am being presumptious ? Do you give us the honor of considering us your friends?"

"Of course, of course," said Yitzchak grandly, "You may ask me anything you like."

"Then would your honor be good enough to tell us why we are journeying to the Land of Moriah?"

"Why ? Why... why... I don't know. I never thought to ask !"

Yitzchak looked so deflated and crestfallen that Peleg and Naor burst into roars of laughter. The little donkey joined in with a metallic bray: Eeeeegh, aaaaargh, eeeeegh, aaaaargh.

Yitzchak was on the verge of tears. He thought to himself, "I am so stupid even the donkey is laughing at me."

Peleg was quick to realize how badly Yitzchak felt. He stopped laughing.

"Don't be downhearted, little chief," he said, "Naor and his stupid jokes. I'd chastise him for you but I've never been able to find a cudgel that woudn't break over his thick head."

Naor growled with mock ferocity.

"You chastise me! Just try it, my fine wrestler and I'll throw you over that palm tree."

"Peleg ! Naor !" Yitzchak could not contain his excitement. "Why are we going to the Land of Moriah ? Do you know ?"

Even Naor grew serious. He said softly, "Know ? Of course we don't know."

"But we can guess a good deal," said Peleg soberly.

"Then why," shrilled Yitzchak, "why are we making this journey to the Land of Moriah ?"

"Because the Lord God commanded it," said Naor.

"Idiot," said Yitzchak impatiently. 'Everything happens because the Lord God commanded it."

Naor was offended. He said, "If we're such idiots, why do you ask us questions ?"

"He didn't say we were idiots," said Peleg judiciously, "He said you were an idiot. I can't say that I disagree with him."

Naor bowed low, with a flourishing sweep of his head scarf.

"My dear friend," he said to Peleg, "You will have to take many lessons before you can become clever enough to be considered an idiot."

Yitzchak regained control of himself with difficulty. He stood quite still and spoke slowly and clearly.

"I want you two to stop squabbling at once and tell me why we are going to the Land of Moriah."

Peleg and Naor looked at each other and grinned.

"He's beginning to sound a little like his father," said Naor.

"More than a little," said Peleg. "The tribe does not have to worry about its next chieftan. Listen, little chief, we think that the Lord God spoke to that holy man, your father, last night and commanded him to make this journey."

Naor nodded soberly.

"It is no small thing for a human being to hear God's voice. Even so great a man as your father is marked by it. It must be a thousand times as painful as putting your hand in the fire."

"And then," continued Peleg, "Your father commanded us to gather wood and chop it into altar lengths and pack it on the donkey's back. Do you know what that means ?"

"Yes," breathed Yitzchak. "A sacrifice. We're going to the land of Moriah to make a sacrifice."

"But what are we going to sacrifice?"

Again, Peleg and Naor looked at each other.

"We don't know," said Peleg slowly, "But we think it will be something of great value."

Chapter VI

"Is everything ready?"

Peleg and Naor leaped to their feet and stood respectfully with eyes cast down at the sound of Abraham's voice. Yitzchak was already standing and he, too, inclined his head respectfully before his father.

There he stood — the leader of the tribe. So intent had the three been on their conversation that they had not heard the swish of his sandals through the sand as he approached them.

"All is ready, chieftan," Peleg answered respectfully.

"Then we start," said Abraham curtly. He turned his face northward and strode resolutely forward. Peleg and Naor hurriedly picked up their spears. Naor seized the leading rope of the donkey and they set out after Abraham.

Yitzchak stood there watching them. He was about to wave goodbye when he realized that this time he, too, was supposed to be going with them. He ran after them, thinking regretfully that he had not had time to say goodbye properly to his mother. He stopped at the first rise and looked backward.

Yitzchak saw his mother, Sarah, standing outside the wall. She stood motionless staring after him. He waved energetically at her. She lifted her hand, let it fall slowly and then went back into the compound.

He stood there, puzzled, until he realized that every member of the tribe not otherwise engaged was watching him. He turned and, with as much dignity as he could muster, strode after his father.

Once over the rise, however, Yitzchak quickly shed his dignity and ran after his travelling companions as quickly as he could. He caught up with Peleg, Naor and the donkey.

"Where are we, Peleg?" he asked.

"We're on the old caravan route to Damascus," Peleg answered.

"Damascus!" his voice had risen as he looked forward to where his father was walking alone, but Abraham seemed not to have heard. "Damascus !" he said again softly, "Will we see Damascus ?"

"No, little chief," said Peleg with a smile, "We'll reach the Land of Moriah long before the route hits Damascus."

"Oh, won't we see any big cities?" asked Yitzchak in disappointment.

"Well, Hebron's on the route. We should reach there tomorrow."

"Is the city walled?"

"Highest walls you've ever seen, little, chief," smiled Peleg.

"And will we go inside?"

"That depends on what the chieftan's plans are. If he's in a hurry we won't go into the city. It takes some time for strangers to get permission to enter the city's walls. If he's in a hurry, we'll just go around it."

"We'll go around it," said Naor suddenly.

"Oh," said Peleg mockingly, "And who told you ?"

"Your friend, the jackass," said Naor straight-faced.

"Ah," said Peleg in mock surprise, 'You can converse with donkeys?"

"No, I leave such higher language studies to you, my fine scholar," said Naor unblinkingly. "But your friend, the jackass, told me anyway."

"I'm afraid I don't understand, Naor."

"I shall try to explain it so simply that even your feeble brain can grasp it. Look at us. Is this fit company for the head of a trible and his only son? Two spearmen and a donkey? Well, one spearman, one donkey and one so-called wrestler."

36

"Wait, father, wait!"

Yitzchak smiled back, his heart filled with wonder.

"Look here, you," said Peleg flushing, "I'll fight you with spears any time you feel like dying."

"I must decline your challenge for two reasons," said Naor soberly. "One, I cannot deprive the tribe of so valuable a member and, two, if I kill you now, who'll carry the load when the donkey gets tired ?"

Yitzchak could contain himself no longer and burst into laughter. After a moment Peleg smiled sheepishly.

"If I may continue without further interruption," said Naor smoothly, "look at us. The chieftan and his son should be riding on camels. They should have a guard of fifty—a hundred—spearmen. Then we could go calling socially on any king in any walled city. But this way, walking like beggars with one donkey, who'd receive us ? That's why I say, we'll go around Hebron, you mark my words."

They continued their journey. Peleg and Naor grumbled under their breath as the sun climbed higher and higher and no word was given to stop and rest. The sun was at its zenith when they finally came to an oasis.

"We stop here," said Abraham. "Take the pack off the donkey and let him graze. We'll go on after we've finished the midday meal."

As soon as Abraham had walked out of earshot,

Peleg grumbled, "Forced marches, as if it were war. What's the burning hurry ?"

"We'll just have to wait and see," said Naor placidly.

Chapter VII

It seemed to Yitzchak that he had been walking forever. On and on and on the weary travellers plodded. After leaving the oasis on the first day, they had walked far into the night and then camped by the roadside. They were up again at daybreak and, after a hasty breakfst, resumed their journey.

It was impossible to tell what Abraham was thinking. He walked forward mechanically, his feet strode with unceasing regularity that ate up the desert distances. Only Yitzchak, sensitive to his father's moods, had the slightest hint as to the turmoil within him. Abraham's face, however, showed nothing of his inner emotion.

At first, Yitzchak had been troubled and puzzled by his father's attitude. He had kept trying to recall something that he might have said or done to make his father angry with him. Try as he might, though, he could not think of anything.

Yitzchak had worried about it at first but, now he was so tired that his brain buzzed when he tried to think. His clothing grew damp with sweat, dried in the hot desert wind, and grew damp again.

"Lord," he prayed silently through clenched teeth, "Oh, the one true God of my father, let me not shame my father and my tribesmen. Give me the strength to keep walking."

"We're coming to the hilly country," said Peleg. "We should be seeing Hebron soon."

"If we're not delayed fighting off the robbers," said Naor.

"Robbers?" said Yitzchak lifting his head. "What robbers?"

"The caravan robbers," said Naor. "They hide behind the hills and lie in wait. When a caravan reaches this spot, they ride down and kill all who oppose them. Then they take whatever they want from the pack saddles and sell the people they've left alive into slavery."

"He's joking, Peleg," said Yitzchak, "isn't he?"

"Not this time," said Peleg seriously. "Hundreds of men have been killed here, they say."

"Who says ?" asked Yitzchak.

"Travellers who've been attacked by the robbers and have escaped them," answered Peleg, "I've talked with dozens of them."

"They won't attack us, though," said Naor positively.

"Why not?" asked Yitzchak.

"They must know that that great hero, Peleg, is travelling with us," said Naor, straight-faced. "It is said that he can kill a hundred robbers with one blow of his spear. And that's with the butt end only. If he ever learns to use a spear properly, he'll be able to kill a thousand."

"No," said Peleg, "We are in great danger if the robbers have heard that that great clown, Naor, is with us. There isn't a king in the world who wouldn't pay a fortune to have him as court jester."

"Pay no attention to my poor friend, Peleg," said Naor. "The robbers don't worry me, little chieftan, but we must look out for the hill monster."

"Hill monster," said Yitzchak startled. "What hill monster?"

"Don't tell me you've never heard of the fabled hill monster, Piflaparmechan," said Naor, his black eyebrows raised in amazement. "I thought everyone knew about him."

"I never heard about Pifla- whatever his name is," said Yitzchak. "Tell me about him, Naor."

"Piflaparmechan, his name is," said Naor in his

sing-song story-telling voice, "and he is awesome to behold. He's as big as a good sized hill and completely covered with hair—each hair as big as a tree. His face is rather revolting, something like Peleg's..."

"Now enough's enough," said Peleg.

"What's that ?" said Yitzchak suddenly.

They stopped and looked in the direction Yitzchak was pointing.

"That, little chief, is the walled city of Hebron," said Peleg, "What do you think of it ?"

It's grand," said Yitzchak. "Oh, to be able to live in a city like that !"

"I like our Beer Sheba better," said Peleg. "She'll be bigger than this some day."

"What did I tell you?" said Naor, "Look, the chief is turning aside. We aren't going through those gates. We're going around the city."

It was true. Abraham had taken a path branching off from the main road that lead toward the main gate of the city. He did not even raise his eyes to look at the city, but walked at his regular rapid pace.

They hurried after him. The donkey brayed his protest at being pulled along so rapidly, which attracted the attention of two soldiers in a watch tower on top of the wall. One of the soldiers pointed them out to his companion and both laughed at the spectacle.

"Come down here, you laughing hyenas," Peleg roared up at them, "I'll give you something to laugh about."

The two soldiers only laughed harder and Peleg shrugged and walked on after the others.

"You're very brave, Peleg," said Yitzchak, "Weren't you afraid to challenge those soldiers ?"

"Little chief," said Peleg, "what is a soldier? He's only a man with a weapon in his hand. Those two looked very grand with their scarlet cloaks and their plumed helmets; but they were only men — and a tribesman of Abraham is as good as any man alive."

"What do you say, Naor," asked Yitzchak. "Wouldn't you be afraid to fight those soldiers?"

"I would agree to fight them only under one condition," said Naor, "and that is if Peleg would help them."

"Peleg help them?" said Yitzchak, "Why?"

"Because he's so clumsy, he'd get in their way and then it would be easy spear sticking."

"Save your foul breath for walking," Peleg growled. "It looks like we'll be doing a lot of it before we stop."

Chapter VII

On and on and on. It was the third day of the journey that Yitzchak had been so happy to embark upon. Again they had had a few hours sleep last night, a quick breakfast, and then they pushed on. On and on and on.

The sun was high in the heavens and they were crossing a valley when Abraham suddenly threw up his hand signalling a halt. His three followers sighed gratefully and threw themselves upon the ground to rest. In front of them loomed Mount Moriah, casting a shadow for which the weary travellers were grateful.

Abraham remained standing and gazed, brooding, at the mountain for a long time. Then his voice cracked out commands:

"Peleg, take the wood from the donkey and make a pack of it. Naor, light a torch. Yitzchak, take the sacrificial knife from the pack and give it to me."

The three leaped to do his bidding. Yitzchak and Peleg had finished their tasks long before Naor accomplished his. Making fire was no easy task in those days. Today, lighting a match or flicking a lighter takes a second to produce flame. It would have seemed like à miracle to Yitzchak.

He watched Naor patiently working his fire making apparatus—the bow whirling the stick, which created heat by friction and ignited the tinder, to which the pitch-smeared torch was applied. Only then did you have flame.

Naor finally accomplished that and gave the burning torch to his tribal leader. Abraham took the torch in one hand and the long sacrificial knife in the other.

"Fasten the wood on Yitzchak's back," Abraham ordered.

The order was obeyed.

"Yitzchak will come with me," Abraham said. "You two will wait here with the donkey until we return."

Peleg and Naor sat down resignedly to wait. Yitzchak straightened up proudly. He was going to help his father sacrifice to the one true God. He trudged up the mountain path after Abraham.

His mind, however, was buzzing with curiosity. As soon as the path widened a bit, he drew even with Abraham and said, a little hesitantly, "Father."

"Yes, my son?"

"Father, we have the wood and the fire—but where is the sacrificial lamb?"

Abraham was silent for a few minutes and finally, after Yitzchak had been sure he was not going to be answered at all, Abraham said softly, "God will provide the sacrificial lamb."

Abraham jammed the torch upright into a cleft where it burned smokily. He placed the sacrificial knife on a ledge beneath it and then removed the pack of wood from Yitzchak's back. Yitzchak stretched gratefully and watched his father go about building an altar.

When all was ready, he turned to his son.

"Yitzchak," he said.

"Yes, my father?"

"Yitzchak, my beloved son. You know how dearly I love you and how precious you are to me."

"I am unworthy, father."

Abraham disregarded the interruption. He continued with difficulty.

"There is only one thing I hold dearer than you, my son, and that is the Lord God, the one true God whom I have followed and obeyed all my life."

"I know, father. I, too, love Him and wish to obey Him."

"Then know, my son, that God has commanded me to bring you to this place and sacrifice you to Him."

Yitzchak stood thunderstruck. The cold fear that he had felt all during the journey seized upon his heart and made him tremble in every limb. He tried to speak, but his tongue would not obey him and his lips were frozen.

Abraham picked up the cords that had bound the wood into a pack and tied Yitzchak securely. He then lifted up his son, held him tenderly for a moment, and placed him upon the altar. Great beads of sweat stood upon his forehead. His eyes seemed misted over and his face was set in a grimace of pain as he walked slowly across the clearing to the ledge and picked up the sacrificial knife.

Yitzchak lay helplessly upon the altar and watched his father come toward him with the sacrificial knife in his hand. He thought, "Poor father, I've never seen him look like this. How he must be suffering."

As Abraham drew closer, Yitzchak found his voice again.

"Father," he said tremulously, "I don't want to die." 70-306

"Your life is dearer to me than my own," said Abraham in a choked voice, but I cannot go against God's command. Are you afraid, my son?"

"Yes, father, I am very much afraid."

"Don't be afraid, son. Death will be quick and merciful. You will feel no pain."

"Wait, father, wait !" Yitzchak had seen his father take a deep breath in preparation for chanting the sacrificial prayer. He knew that, once that prayer started, nothing could stop the shining knife from rising and falling and snuffing out his life.

"Wait, father, couldn't you be mistaken?"

"No, son, I made no mistake. I heard God's command clearly."

"Father, call upon Him again. Here! Now! Ask Him to change His mind, to revoke His command."

"I cannot do that, my son."

"Why not? Why not? Father, do you want to kill me?

"Yitzchak, my son," Abraham groaned in agony, "God must be obeyed without question. That is why He is God and we are men. He must be ebeyed!"

Yitzchak closed his eyes. There was nothing more he could say. He had to die. The more he struggled, the more he pleaded, the more he added to his father's suffering. His father understood even less than he did why he must die. He knew only that God must be obeyed.

"So be it," Yitzchak sighed resignedly, "Blessed be the name of the Lord."

He heard the tear-choked voice of his father start the sacrificial chant. At the end of the chant the knife would descend.

"Why are my eyes closed," he thought, "How cowardly I am to be afraid to look at the knife that will take my life! Open your eyes, Yitzchak son of Abraham. Look for the last time at the sky, the clouds, the trees, the earth!"

With a great effort, Yitzchak opened his eyes. And saw the glory of the angel of the Lord appear in the sky.

Chapter VIII

It was the most beautiful sight Yitzchak had ever seen—or ever would see. An indescribable radiance filled the sky; but deeper, purer, more glowing than man ordinarily saw.

The angel looked directly into Yitzchak's eyes and smiled at him. Yitzchak smiled back, his heart filled with wonder and with love for the one true God who had such marvellous, perfect beings at His command. Yitzchak began to understand a little the love and worship his father felt toward his God.

Had this beautiful angel come to lead him to God? If so, how foolish to fear death! Was he already dead? No. Tearing his eyes away from the angel's face, Yitzchak looked at his father.

Lines of suffering were etched black in Abraham's face. He had come to the end of the sacrificial chant and, with a sob tearing his throat, he raised the knife high. The blade glittered in the sun. With only a fraction of a second's hesitation, Abraham started the downswing of the knife—the stroke that would kill his only, beloved son, that would complete the sacrifice of the precious life God demanded of him.

The knife stopped in mid-air as though held by an invisible force. Abraham's muscles strained to complete the blow—to no avail. Then the angel spoke. The beauty of his voice matched the radiance of his appearance. No human ears had ever heard such music. The sound throbbed. You heard it not only with your ears, but with your entire being.

"Abraham !"

Abraham stopped stock-still. He straightened up and slowly turned about to face the angel.

"Abraham," said the angel of the Lord, "do not harm the boy. You have proved your devotion to God's command. You were willing to give Him your only son. God is satisfied."

The angel vanished. Abraham stood stunned for a long moment. Then the knife slipped from his hand. He steadied himself against the side of the altar as though to keep from falling and then sat down slowly by the altar's side, supporting his head in his hands. His entire body shook with dry, racking sobs.

From the altar where he lay bound, Yitzchak watched his father, first with amazement and then with understanding.

"He's crying," he thought. 'Father's crying because he's happy that he doesn't have to kill me. Oh, my father! My wonderful father!"

Strength flowed through Yitzchak's body. He strained at his bonds and they snapped as though they were straw. He sat up and the blood coursed singing through his body. He jumped off the stone altar and went down on his knees near his father.

Abraham was the first to recover. He rose, assuming his customary stern authority.

"An altar has been prepared for a sacrifice to the Lord," he said. "A sacrifice must be made. Otherwise, it would be an offense to the Lord."

Yitzchak saw a movement in the underbrush not far off. He pointed.

"Father, look. What is that ?"

They both went over to the spot. It was a ram. His horns were caught in a thicket and he was plunging this way and that way, trying to free himself. Abraham seized the ram, tied its legs together and placed it upon the altar. The ram bleated and rolled its eyes in terror.

"Poor ram," thought Yitzchak, "he wants to live, too. I know just how he feels."

Abraham picked up the knife where he had dropped it. He began the sacrificial chant and, at its end, plunged the knife with one quick, clean sweep that cut the ram's throat. Then he put the torch to the wood, lighing a blaze which consumed the ram's body.

Watching the smoke rise skyward, Yitzchak thought, "That might have been me. Why does God want living creatures killed? What is the point of a sacrifice? Does killing add to the glory of God? I don't understand why God demands sacrifices."

Yitzchak had seen many lambs and bullocks sacrificed and had enjoyed the excitement and the religious feeling of an offering to God. It was just that he never before had thought of the proceeding from the victim's point of view.

Abraham broke in upon his thoughts by saying, "Come, my son. Our work here is done. We shall go down and return home."

As they turned to go, the angel of the Lord appeared before them again. Father and son stood speechless at the sight of such heavenly glory. The angel spoke:

"These are the words of the Lord: You have been tested and found true. You have not withheld your son, your only son, from Me. Because you have obeyed My voice, you shall be blessed.

"Your tribe shall increase and your nation shall be great. Your people shall be as numerous as the stars of the heavens and the sands of the seashore. They shall be a blessing to all the nations of the earth.

"These are the words of the Lord."

The angel stopped speaking and was gone.

Father and son walked down the descending path together. Halfway down, they stopped and looked back. The mountain top looked peaceful. God's spirit rested there.

He drew himself up and glared.

"It is a gift from Ziphaiah."

Chapter IX

As he walked down the mountain at his father's side, Yitzchak found himself thinking more deeply than he ever had before. His head was buzzing with questions and speculations and, when he could not find the answer in his own brain, he turned to his father.

"Father," he said, "I should like to ask a question."

One of his rare smiles lit up Abraham's countenance. It reflected the love he felt for his son and his gratitude that he had been spared.

"Speak, my son," said Abraham.

"Why does God test us, father?"

As Abraham's face grew stern and he opened his mouth to speak, Yitzchak hurried on, "Father, it's not enough to say God's ways must not be questioned. I know that. God is God and must be obeyed.

"Father, listen to me. I love you and obey you. Is it wrong for me to try to understand you? If I understand why you say things and do things, will I not love you more and obey you more readily?

"And isn't it the same with God, who is the Father of us all? If I question—not in mockery, not in doubt—but with a real desire to understand, is that wrong? Is that wrong, father?"

Abraham looked at the young, earnest, glowing face turned up toward him. He reflected that, suddenly, his son had ceased to be a child and had become a young man.

"You speak well, my son," said Abraham slowly. "No. In that spirit, in the spirit of trying to understand, it is not wrong to ask questions about God. Always remembering," he raised his hand warningly as Yitzchak opened his mouth to speak, "always remembering that man can never completely understand God."

"But it is permitted," persisted Yitzchak. "It is permitted to try to come closer to understanding and so increase our love for God."

"Yes," said Abraham.

"Father," Yitzchak's voice was deeper and more reflective, "God sees the past, the present and the future. He knows everything that has happened, that is happening, that will happen."

"True," said Abraham.

"Then why does God test man," Yitzchak burst forth, "Why does He test man in pain and suffering when He knows in advance whether man will pass the test or fail it ? He knows, father, He knows in advance! He knows how everything will turn out! Isn't the pain and suffering that He puts man through in testing him useless? Isn't God guilty of needless cruelty ?"

"Yitzchak," said Abraham warningly.

"We have a right to question," interrupted Yitzchak hotly. "We have a right to know. We have suffered pain in the testing. We have a duty to try to understand why !"

Abraham gazed in amazement at this angry, young man—insistent in his questions, demanding answers. Was this his son? Was this his Yitzchak, who had acsended Mount Moriah at his side, a happy, carefree boy?

"Why, he's almost as tall as I am," thought Abraham. "He's been growing up right under my eyes and I never even noticed."

Aloud, he said, "Yitzchak, let us continue down the mountain."

Together, they continued their descent in silence for some time. Then Abraham spoke, slowly and reflectively.

"My son, how many times have you climbed a tree just to see how high you could climb ? How many times have you leaped over a ditch just to see how far you could leap ?"

"Many times, father," answered Yitzchak.

"If I had told you : Yitzchak, there is no need for you to climb that tree. I know you can climb it. There is no need for you to try to jump over that ditch. I know you can do it. If I had said that, what would you have done ?"

Yitzchak thought for a long moment and then said, "I think I would have climbed that tree anyway. And jumped over the ditch, too. Just to see for myself if I could do it."

"But," said Abraham, "you knew you could do it. I told you you could do it. You believe what I tell you, don't you ?"

"Yes, father," Yitzchak's brow was furrowed in thought. "I believe you but I still think I would have tried to do it just so I could see for myself."

Abraham smiled. Yitzchak slowly smiled back at him.

"Do you understand what I'm trying to say, my son?" said Abraham.

"I think so, father," said Yitzchak, "but I'm not sure. Please explain it to me."

"No, Yitzchak," said Abraham. "Jump over the ditch for yourself. You explain it to me."

Yitzchak tood a deep breath, then plunged forward groping for an explanation.

"I think," he said slowly, "I think you mean that God tests man, not for His own sake, but for man's sake."

"Go on," said Abraham, as Yitzchak hesitated.

"God knows whether man can pass the test," said Yitzchak, "but man doesn't know. And he must know, even at the cost of pain and suffering. Just as I had to know whether I could climb that tree, even if I slipped and got bruised, even if I fell and came home bleeding and crying to mother to bind up my wounds."

He walked straight and tall at his father's side as they came down from the mountain and walked into camp. Peleg and Naor jumped to their feet, glad to see them, grateful for their safety.

"God be praised," said Abraham in answer to their words. "All is well. Prepare the evening meal. We shall camp here tonight and start for home in the morning."

At the first opportunity, Peleg and Naor sidled over to where Yitzchak was patting the donkey and questioned him breathlessly.

"Did you sacrifice?" asked Peleg.

"Yes," said Yitzchak.

"What did you sacrifice?" asked Naor.

"A ram," answered Yitzchak.

"What ram ?" said Naor, "Where did you get a ram ?"

"God sent it," said Yitzchak.

"Did you see God ?" asked Peleg, wide-eyed.

"No," said Yitzchak, smiling as their faces fell, "but I did see an angel."

Chapter X

All the way home, as the travellers retraced the route by which they had come, it was Yitzchak who was in the lead. He would have been horrified if someone had pointed out to him that it was a mark of disrespect to his father, as head of the tribe, to have anyone walk ahead of him at any time.

Abraham, walking after his son, understood what was bothering the young boy. So much had happened to him in so short a time. He had passed through so much strangeness. Now he wanted to feel once more the familiarity of things long known.

Yitzchak had grown up so quickly in the past few days. He wanted to hold on a bit longer to the familiar things of his childhood. He felt that if only he were at home now—right this minute —

it would still the feeling of unease that he felt within him.

So he pushed on as quickly as he could and bit his lip with impatience whenever Abraham called a halt for rest or food. He would wolf down his share of the meal and then would be in a fever to be on the move again.

At one stop, the donkey had found a patch of succulent grass and was grazing contentedly. Yitzchak felt he could not wait another second to continue the homeward journey. He pulled the donkey roughly away and began to put the pack saddle on him.

Naor, lying contentedly on his back chewing a blade of grass, drawled lazily, "Little chief, you finished your meal, let the donkey finish his."

Yitzchak dropped the donkey's halter and turned around to face Naor. He drew himself up and glared at him wordlessly. After a long moment, Naor lumbered to his feet and assumed a respectful stance.

"Your pardon, little chief," he rumbled, "I meant no disrespect."

Yitzchak did not answer nor did he relax the sternness of his expression. He turned on his heel and walked off a little way, gazing southward,

southward—always southward—toward Beer Sheba.

Peleg nudged Naor and they both set about
saddling the donkey.

"It's a good thing you apologized," Peleg grinned.
"He would have killed you on the spot if you
hadn't."

Naor grinned back. He was too happy to pretend
to fight with Peleg. It was a good thing for the tribe
to have a young chieftan with spirit. Naor had
been a little worried. Yitzchak was a good boy but
he had been—well, just a bit of a namby-pamby.

Not any more, though. By the one true living
God, no! Whatever had happened on that mountain
top had changed the little chief right enough. He
was all fire now.

He was still musing over the change in Yitzchak
as they continued on their journey. He looked up
to make sure that Abraham and Yitzchak were
far enough in the lead to be out of earshot and
then spoke to Peleg in an undertone, "What do you
suppose really happened on that mountain ?"

"Your guess is a good as mine," shrugged Peleg.
"Whatever it was, it sure changed the little chief."

"He says he saw an angel," Naor said reflectively.

"Maybe he did," said Peleg. "Maybe seeing an
angel makes you act like one."

"There's a lot to what you say, Peleg," said Naor with disarming seriousness. "You've been looking at a donkey's backside for some time now and I'm beginning to notice the resemblance."

At last, at long last, Beer Sheba came into view. Yitzchak could contain himself no longer. He ran over the sand to where the tribe was drawn up to welcome their returning leader. He ran straight to Sarah and embraced her.

"Mother, dear mother," he said, "I'm glad to see you again."

To his hurt surprise, she made no answer, acting as though he had not spoken and as though she were unaware of his presence. He drew back, puzzled and confused. What had he done to offend his mother ?

Abraham came into view then and the whole tribe cheered its welcome. He approached Sarah, who bowed low before him and said, "Welcome home, my lord." She straightened up and received his kiss gratefully. He then went on to greet other members of the tribe.

Only then did Sarah turn to Yitzchak and smile at him. Her smile was full of love and heart-warming motherly affection.

"Welcome home, my son," she said.

A wave of shame and humiliation swept over

Yitzchak. He realized what he had done, what an offense he had committed before the entire assembled tribe. He had preceded the head of the tribe and demanded a greeting before the chieftan had been officially welcomed. Sarah had been kind and very lenient in merely ignoring him. His offense called for much more serious punishment.

The old Yitzchak—that is to say, the younger Yitzchak—would have run away to hide his shame. He might have brooded and sulked for a week. The new Yitzchak mastered himself after a short inner struggle, advanced to his mother, and bowed before her.

"Greetings, honored mother," he said with dignity. "It is good to be home."

Sarah looked at her son closely. She realized, with surprise, that she had to look up to see his face.

"He's grown up," she thought, "My son has grown up. I used to call him my big boy in fun. And now the joke has become the truth."

Seeing Yitzchak every day, his mother did not realize how he had grown. The short separation brought it home to her with a shock. But the change in him was more than mere size, she thought. He seemed to have grown up inside as well as outside.

"The trip has done you good, my son," said Sarah.

"Yes, mother," said Yitzchak, "I have seen much and learned a little."

"What have you learned, my son?"

"It's difficult to put into words, mother."

"Try, my son."

"Well, when I was a little boy..." Sarah suppressed a smile. Yitzchak noticed it but went on. "When I was a little boy, I thought father was the greatest man in the world and I wanted to be like him."

"And now, my son?"

"I still think father is the greatest man in the world. But I don't want to be like him any more. I want to be me."

Sarah looked at her son for a long while, then she said softly, "Come and eat, Yitzchak, son of Abraham."

Chapter XI

The years passed—seemingly slowly when lived through day by day, but seemingly quickly when one looked back and wondered where the time had gone. No one really knew how many years. In those days, no written records were kept. In fact, hardly anyone knew how to write.

Also, writing materials weren't very plentiful. If anyone wanted to make a note of anything, the accepted thing to do was to cut it in stone. That took time and trouble and it had to be something pretty important to be considered worthwhile to note down.

That may be the reason we read in the bible of people living to fantastic, improbable ages. If may be that people lived longer in those days. It might also very well be that people didn't count the years very accurately, because they depended on their memory and the memory of man is sometimes unreliable.

In any event, the years passed—unrecorded except in the faces of the people. The years left their mark on Yitzchak's parents. Abraham and Sarah were visibly older, though they carried their years well.

Yitzchak, too, was changed by time. He was grown now-well set-up, straight and serious. He had put childish things behind him. He had been initiated into the tribe and, on appropriate occasions, he preached about the one true God of the tribe of Abraham. Everyone remarked upon how well he spoke.

68

They were good years for the tribe of Abraham. The people prospered and their numbers increased. The city of Beer Sheba grew, too, along with its inhabitants. The city settled in and spread out.

Yitzchak was conscientious about training himself to lead the tribe. He considered physical fitness very important to a tribal leader and he exercised every day with his teachers, Peleg and Naor.

He wasn't able to throw Peleg yet, but he knew all of the wrestling holds and was able to give him a bit of trouble. More and more lately, Peleg found himself unable to throw Yitzchak, strain as he might. And the sweating Peleg would pant, "Enough for today, little chief. Your progress is very satisfactory."

Naor, too, found him a satisfactory pupil. Yitzchak could throw a spear far and accurately and, in hand to hand fighting, Naor had to move his shield rapidly to ward off his pupil's spear point. They would spend hours, as well, circling each other warily with dummy, wooden knives in their hands, lunging and cutting. Naor was considered the best knife fighter of the tribe and he taught Yitzchak faithfully and well, finding him tough and quick. After he had been teaching Yitzchak for some time, Naor admitted to himself — and to no one else— that he would not like to have to fight Yitzchak with real knives.

The basis upon which the tribe's prosperity was built was — sheep. The flocks grew fat and increased because they were well tended and carefully guarded. Yitzchak took his turn in guarding the sheep against wild animals and human marauders.

That was one of the things that made people like Yitzchak. He didn't, as we call, nowadays, "pull rank." He was the only son of the head of the tribe. He would some day lead the tribe. But he gave himself no airs. He acted just like any other young man in the tribe and did his tour of guard duty cheerfully and well.

Another, an increasingly important, source of income for the tribe was the caravan trade. As the city of Beer Sheba developed, the camel caravans made a point of stopping over—and trade was brisk.

In those days, goods were moved from one point to another—from the seller to the buyer—on camel back across the desert. Robbers were numerous and merchants would travel in bands called caravans, with enough men to be able to defend their lives and their property against desert marauders.

Yitzchak, acting as his father's deputy, often was

called upon to welcome the caravans to the city and see to it that they were made comfortable and treated fairly. Once the word got around among the caravan leaders that a place was dangerous or inhospitable, that place was given a wide berth by the caravans. So, since part of the tribe's livelihood depended upon commerce, Yitzchak's work was important.

He liked this aspect of his duties. He liked sitting around the fire at night with the camel drivers and merchants, listening to them tell tall tales of faraway places, of fierce fights with desert robbers, and the splendors of the cities where they sold their goods.

One evening, one of the merchants approached Yitzchak and said to him, "Pardon, young prince, I have been told that Sarah, wife of Abraham, lives in this city. Could you tell me where I can find her ? I have a message for her."

"I am her son," said Yitzchak. "You may give me the message."

"Excellent," said the merchant. "That saves me a lot of time and trouble. Here," he produced a package from the voluminous folds of his garment, "please give this to your good mother and tell her that it is a gift from her old friend, Ziphaiah, wife of Gibeon of the city of Hebron. She asks to be remembered to her old girlhood friend and hopes all is well with her. I was entrusted with this packet and commissioned to deliver it. I shall be grateful if you will take it from me so that I can sleep now. We make an early start tomorrow and I am tired."

Yitzchak took the package from the merchant and, after a few more polite exchanges, took his leave and brought the package to his mother.

Sarah was enchanted with the gift, a beautiful gown cleverly embroidered with gold and silver thread.

"Silly Ziphaiah," Sarah laughed. "She always was feather headed. Sending me a gown like this at my age. This is for a young girl. She must think I'm the same girl she knew so many years ago."

"You are a beautiful woman, my mother," said Yitzchak, "I am sure the gown will become you."

"Nonsense," said Sarah, trying not to show how pleased she was, "I am an old woman. I'll save this gown. Your bride will wear it. Oh, but I'd like to see Ziphaiah again. She was my dearest friend when we were young, silly girls together. She was given in marriage to a lord of the tribe of Chait and I

Eliezer wondered what he was supposed to do now.

The girl went straight to the well.

haven't seen her from that day to this. She lives in Hebron, the merchant said ?"

"Yes, mother."

"Why, that isn't far at all. I'd love to go visit her. I wonder if I could get your father to give me permission to make the trip."

Abraham was not easily persuaded. He could not be spared at this particular time to make the journey and he hesitated to entrust her safety to anyone else. The roads were dangerous. Sarah was getting on in years. Such a journey was bound to be difficult for her.

Sarah answered that she never had felt better in her life. Just the thought of seeing her dear friend made her feel like a young girl again. As for the rest of it, she had a wonderful idea. Put Yitzchak in command of her bodyguard. Abraham's objections were overcome, one by one.

"Take thirty spearmen," he said to Yitzchak. "Pick them yourself. I can let you have camels for the entire party. That should make it easier. Remember when we made the journey on foot ?"

"Yes, father." The two smiled at one another. Then Abraham's face resumed its stern aspect.

"I shall hold you personally responsible for your mother's safety," Abraham said.

"I understand my responsibility," said Yitzcak. "I shall live up to it."

Word of Sarah's trip spread quickly and Peleg and Naor came to Yitzchak, clamoring to be taken along. Yitzchak knew why. Reumah was to be one of the maids in Sarah's entourage. She had grown up to be rather pretty and had lately been saucily distributing her smiles equally between Peleg and Naor.

"Look, you two," said Yitzchak, "if you're going to be making sheep's eyes at that wench all the time, you'll be of no use to me whatsoever."

"I won't have to make sheep's eyes at her, little chief," said Naor. "Once she gets a good look at Peleg's ugly face, she'll come flying into my arms in terror."

Yitzchak laughed and put their names down at the head of the list.

Chapter XII

Actually, Hebron is the modern name of the city that was called, in Yitzchak's day, "Kiryat Arba." In Hebrew, the name means "The City of Four." According to the legend, the city was founded by a very large giant and his three sons, who were also giants, but not quite so huge as their father.

There was no trouble about gaining admittance at the city's gate, with a tribal notable like Gibeon to vouch for them. The reunion between Sarah and Ziphaiah took place in a flurry of embraces, tears and laughter. Sarah was whisked away to be entertained in the women's quarters of Gibeon's very grand house. Sarah's maids unpacked the camels and followed their mistress. Reumah received a great deal of unnecessary assistance from Peleg and Naor right up to the door of the mansion, where she entered with a dazzling smile flung over her shoulder at both of them.

Yitzchak superintended the setting of the tent encampment not far from the house, where the guards would stay. He then posted sentries, drew up a roster of the men assigned to sentry duty, turned over the command to Peleg and Naor so that one officer would always be on duty and gave the rest of the men leave to go sightseeing in the city. He warned them sternly to stay out of trouble and not get into any fights with any of the strutting guards of the city. A blood feud between tribes could be a very ugly business.

His duty done for the moment, Yitzchak entered the house, as the ranking male member of the tribe of Abraham to pay his respects to the lord of the manor. He was received graciously and given a room where he could wash, change and rest from the rigors of his journey.

He was invited to a banquet that evening where he met with some of the notables of the tribe of Chait. His manly demeanor made a good impression upon the leading men of the Chait tribe and a preliminary discussion was started regarding closer association and cooperation between the two tribes.

Sarah, of course, sat modestly in the background with the women. Her dear friend, Ziphaiah, had no sooner set eyes upon Sarah's handsome son when she formed her own ideas about closer association and cooperation between the two tribes. She had a daughter about Yitzchak's age. A whispered word into the ear of one of her maids and the daughter appeared shortly thereafter and took her place among the women. Ziphaiah had decided she wasn't too young to attend the party after all.

Sarah smiled grimly to herself. Ziphaiah was going to a lot of trouble for nothing. Abraham has some very strong ideas about intermarriage with the Canaanites. The girl was pretty, though, and Yitzchak noticed her immediately and kept glancing her way every now and then.

"How tiresome," thought Sarah. "Another complication. I'll have to think how to deal with it tomorrow. I'm just too tired tonight."

Making her excuses to her hostess, she retired to her quarters, followed by her retinue of maids.

In the morning, Yitzchak was awakened by one of the manservants of the house. The man blurted out, "Your mother is dead," and dashed away.

Yitzchak rubbed the sleep from his eyes and ran to the women's quarters. Ordinarily, a strange man attempting to enter this part of the house would have been killed immediately. Now, however, all was chaos. Women were wailing and guards were scurrying about it confusion.

He made his way to his mother's room, brushed aside the weeping maids, and knelt by her bedside. The dear, familiar, beloved face was already turning waxen. He touched her hand. It was cold as ice.

Blindly, he made his way to his room and threw himself on his bed. The tears finally came and he sobbed out his heartbreak. He did not know how long he cried, but he finally became aware of Peleg standing in the doorway.

"Peleg," he said brokenly "my old friend, Peleg."

"Begging your pardon, Yitzchak son of Abraham," grated Peleg harshly. "At this moment I am not your old friend, Peleg. I am a soldier under your command. It was our duty to guard our chieftan's wife. She is dead. What are your orders, commander ?"

It was like stepping under an icy torrent. Yitzchak gasped. The cold contempt in Peleg's voice was exactly what he needed. He felt a surge of rage and controlled it. He stood up and spoke in a tone of formal command.

"My father must be notified immediately. Send a messenger at once. My mother's..." he almost broke down, but regained control of himself, "My mother's body must be prepared for burial. See to it. Dimissed."

"Your orders will be obeyed, commander." Peleg turned smartly and marched off.

As a matter of fact, Naor had dispatched a trustworthy man on their fastest camel to Beer Sheba minutes after they had heard the news. Peleg, entering the women's quarters found that Reumah had taken charge. Although one of the youngest of Sarah's women, she was the only one who kept her head. She slapped some sense into the heads of the hysterically wailing women and they set about, weeping but efficient, to prepare Sarah's body for her last journey.

Peleg and Naor, in unspoken conspiracy, contrived to keep their young chief busy. He was called upon to inspect his men, to approve or disapprove of every detail of every arrangment. He was required to stand at the head of his men and receive delegation after delegation of notables of the tribe of Chait, offering their condolences.

So the days passed until Abraham arrived. Yitzchak received him at the head of his men. Abraham dismounted and looked long and hard at his son. Again Yitzchak felt, as he had when he was a child, that Abraham could look into his heart and see what was hidden there. At last, Abraham said quietly, "Come with me, my son."

They both went to where Sarah was lying. Father and son wept and mourned together. Then Abraham rose and said, "Enough of mourning, my son, there are many things to be done."

Yitzchak went out with his father and found the tribesmen of Chait assembled before the gate of the city. He was surprised to see how many of them knew his father or, at least, had heard of him. They showed marked respect for Abraham and condoled with him upon the loss of his wife.

Abraham, dignified in his grief, spoke respectfully to the tribe of Chait and asked them to help him to acquire a tomb where he might bury his dead. Yitzchak was amazed at Abraham's knowledge of the country when Abraham went on to say

81

that he knew of a cave in a field owned by Ephron, son of Zohar, a Hittite living among the tribe of Chait.

Ephron himself stepped forward and offered to give the field to Abraham. Abraham replied politely that he could not accept so valuable a gift and insisted upon paying the full price for it. Ephron said that the field was worth four hundred shekels of silver and Abraham promptly paid him.

Then the funeral cortege moved to the field of Ephron, the field called Machpelah, before Mamre in the city of Hebron. Sarah's bier was carried past the trees and into the cave upon the shoulders of her tribesmen. And there she was placed in her final resting place.

Father and son stood a long time before Sarah's tomb. Then Abraham put his hand upon Yitzchak's shoulder.

"Come, my son," he said. "It's time to go home."

Chapter XIII

Once his father appeared, the burden of command fell from Yitzchak's shoulders. It was the need to control himself and do his duty that had stiffened the young man's spine and kept his head erect. Now he relaxed almost to the point of complete collapse.

Yitzchak had loved his mother very much and her sudden death was a severe blow to him. One evening he had seen her sitting with the other ladies at a feast, laughing and chatting — his own sweet, charming, gracious mother. The next morning she was cold, lifeless clay.

Yitzchak brooded and grieved. His interest could not be roused for anything. He seemed to be merely going through the motions of living. All the members of the tribe were concerned and troubled. The chieftan was an old man. He might die any day. Yitzchak, in his present state, was unfit to lead the tribe.

Abraham knew exactly what was going on. His body was ageing, but his brain was as keen as ever. His eyes did not miss much and his brain knew how to interpret what he saw.

He called the chief steward of his household to him and said, "Eliezer, we must find my son a wife."

Marriages were arranged by parents in those days and for centuries thereafter. The children had little or no say in choosing their husbands and wives. The system seemed to work as well as computer dating does nowadays.

It was not until the nineteenth century that the romantic and revolutionary notion arose that love and marriage should go together and that boys and girls should choose whom they were going to marry.

So Eliezer did not blink at his master's statement. Finding a wife for the chief's son was not something to be taken lightly. He thought for a moment and then said, "When Yitzchak visited the house of Gibeon in Hebron, there was a daughter there that seemed to find favor in his eyes."

"No !" thundered Abraham. "Our line must not intermingle with that of the Canaanites. They worship false gods. If my son were to marry a Canaanite girl it would anger our one true God. You must go to my country and find my son a wife from among my kinsmen."

Now if Eliezer had a fault, it was an enormous lack of self-confidence. He was horrified at his master's command.

"I ?" he croaked. "Oh, no, good master! I am unfit for so delicate a task. I am afraid I would not choose wisely."

"The Lord God will guide you," said Abraham.

"The angel of the Lord will walk before you and smooth the way."

Eliezer blinked rapidly. He foresaw a dozen difficulties; and he was sure that there were several dozen that he had not foreseen.

'Good master," gulped Eliezer, "let us say that the Lord God guides me and the angel of the Lord walks before me. Let us say that I find the right girl and arrange a suitable match. I don't for a moment believe I can, but let's say so for the sake of argument. Suppose, as is quite likely, the girl refuses to leave the big city and come out here to live in the desert? In that case, Yitzchak had better come with me so that the marriage can take place soon after it is arranged and the young couple can settle down in the city among your kinsmen."

"No," said Abraham decisively. "The God of heaven and earth told me to leave the city of my birth. He said that my destiny and the destiny of my people lies here in the land of Canaan, which He would give to us. Yitzchak stays here."

"But, suppose..."

"If you can't find a suitable girl," Abraham interrupted a flow of objections at its source, "then your part of the job is over. You come back here and we'll look elsewhere."

"Good master, consider..."

"You will leave tomorrow," said Abraham.

It isn't advisable to argue with one's boss today. In those days, it was impossible. Unhealthy, too. Eliezer bowed and withdrew to make ready for the journey.

Despite his lack of self-confidence, Eliezer was a wily trader, a keen negotiator and—although the word hadn't been invented yet—something of a psychologist. He took ten camels from Abraham's herd, dressed them richly, and piled them high with costly gifts. That was to bedazzle the prospective in-laws with his master's wealth. For the rest, he would depend on his own eloquent tongue and the angel of the Lord who would surely give him a sign of some sort. Hadn't his master, Abraham, said so?

Eliezer also picked the best camel-drivers in the tribe to accompany him. That was wise. The camel is not an easy animal to get along with. A camel-driver has to be good at his job or there's trouble.

To Western eyes, the camel is a monstrosity of a creature — weirder than a giraffe and several times as outlandish. He has a neck like a fuzzy python, which joins a body shaped like a four legged Hunchback of Notre Dame. His face is set in a permanent sneer and he smells like a garbage dump on a hot, muggy day.

The camel is so gosh-darned big ! To get on his back, you either have to use a ladder—and you have no guarantee that the camel would stand still while you were climbing up—or you have to convince the camel to kneel down. To do that, a camel-driver makes a noise that is a cross between a click and a growl, a snarl and a howl. To get the camel to his feet again, the camel-driver makes the same kind of noise, only in reverse.

If getting onto a camel is complicated, getting off is downright hazardous. The camel-driver makes that peculiar sound. The camel lurches to his front knees and then sinks to his rear axle. The resulting motion is reminiscent of the pitching and tossing of a small boat during a winter storm in the North Atlantic. After that, if you haven't already been thrown off, and you can manage to overcome your seasickness, you dismount.

Fortunately, desert transport is being taken over in modern times by the motor truck and the tractor. The camel is slowly becoming an exotic relic, like the horse, the elephant, and the water buffalo— still used by peasants in the outlying boondocks. Come to the camel market in Beer Sheba on the right day and you can get your picture taken sitting on a camel, if you go in for that sort of thing.

However, for hundreds of years before the

invention of the gasoline motor, man could not have crossed the desert without this ugly, evil-tempered, foul-smelling beast. And camel-drivers loved their camels. If they wanted to pay tribute to a girl's beauty, they would say, "She is as beautiful as a camel !"

So Eliezer picked the best camel-drivers for his crew and the little caravan travelled to the land between two rivers. They stopped outside the city gates and dismounted near the well in the center of the square. Eliezer scratched himself, looked about, and wondered what he was supposed to do now.

"Lord God," he prayed, looking heavenward, "give me a sign. Angel of the Lord, please appear —as my master promised—and tell me what to do."

The heavens were silent and no angel appeared.

"Very well, then," said Eliezer to himself, "I shall make up my own sign. I shall stand here by the well and the first maiden that comes here to draw water, I will say to her, 'Excuse me, young lady, may I have a drink from your pitcher?" And she will answer, "Of course, good sir, please drink, and I shall fill up the trough with my pitcher so that your camels may drink." That will be the sign that she is the girl the Lord God intends for my master's son, Yitzchak."

Eliezer was pleased with himself. That was a pretty good sign he had made up all by himself, without help from any angel. Then his jaw dropped.

A beautiful young girl, her eyes modestly downcast, was coming to the well with a pitcher on her shoulder.

Chapter XIV

The girl, seemingly unaware that a number of strange men were staring at her with wide eyes and open mouths, went straight to the well and let down her pitcher to fill it. She was used to being stared at. Most pretty girls get used to it after a while.

Eliezer licked his lips, took a deep breath, and swallowed several times to overcome the dryness of his throat, which was caused by more than the dust he had swallowed during the journey. Good Lord, this might be the girl his master had sent him to find ! Now to test the sign he had made up. He approached the girl at the well.

"Excuse me, young lady," he croaked. "May I have a drink from your pitcher ?"

"Of course, good sir," she answered politely.

Eliezer took the pitcher she held out to him and let the clear, cool water run down his throat.

"When you have finished drinking," the girl said, "I shall fill up the trough with my pitcher so that your camels may drink."

Eliezer almost choked on his drink and handed back the pitcher spluttering. That was it! That was the sign! The girl had given the exact answers. By the one, true, living God of Abraham, the angel might just as well be pointing his finger. Eliezer looked up, half expecting to see an angel pointing. No, he couldn't see one, but he was sure the angel must be there just out of sight.

The girl had finished filling the trough and the camels lumbered up and buried their ugly muzzles in the water, drinking as though they would never stop. Eliezer went over to where the girl was standing. He bowed to her and said, "You have been very polite and helpful, my child, please accept these baubles as a slight token of my appreciation."

He handed her two bracelets and an earing. They were made of heavy gold and beautifully wrought. She took them, exclaiming with pleasure at their beauty, as women have done since the beginning of time—and will probably go on doing until the end of time.

"What is you name, my child?" asked Eliezer.

Water to wash their feet...

"These are Abraham's gifts to his kinsmen."

"I am called Rivka, daughter of Bethuel," she answered absently, putting the bracelets on her wrists and watching them glisten in the sun.

Eliezer almost staggered. He knew the girl although he had never seen her before. Her father Bethuel was the son of Milcah, who was the daughter of Nahor, Abraham's brother.

The angel of the Lord had led him directly to the daughter of his master's kinsmen. Blessed be the name of the Lord !

"Tell me, my dear child," said Eliezer tremulously, "is there room in your father's house for us to stay? We are weary travellers who have come a long way."

"Oh, yes," said Rivka. "We have plenty of room. And fodder for your camels and food for you and your men. Wait here."

Rivka had reached her house and showed her presents to her mother. Both of them uttered fluting cries of admiration for the beauty of the ornaments.

Rivka's brother, Lavan, happened to be passing and asked what the excitement was about. Rivka told him the story and showed him the bracelets and the earring. Lavan thoughtfully weighed them in his hand and scratched the surface with his thumbnail. Real gold—and of the highest quality!

A man who could casually hand out gifts like that wasn't a pauper!

Lavan was still young, but he was already acquiring the reputation of a shrewd trader. He made a beeline for the city gates. As he came through the gates, he spotted the caravan. His eyes made a quick appraisal of the camels, their trappings, and the contents of their packs. He then came forward and bowed to Eliezer.

"Greetings, worthy sir," Lavan said, "I can see at a glance that you are blessed of the Lord. Why are you standing out here? Please come in and accept the humble hospitality of my father's house. Please, this way."

Lavan led them through the streets of the city, chattering all the way.

"This is an honor for my father's house. Come along. I have prepared everything. There is plenty of room. And fodder for your animals, fine camels they are, must have cost a pretty penny."

He led them to the stables and helped them to unsaddle and feed the camels. Then he gave Eliezer and his men water to wash their feet.

Now, that may sound a little peculiar to Western ears and calls for a little explanation. Giving a guest water to wash his feet was the standard form of greeting in the code of hospitality of the desert. If the guest was a very honored one, the host washed the guest's feet himself—and dried them.

The original reason for the custom is not hard to determine. A man's feet got pretty dirty, travelling in the sandy desert. And water was precious. What better way to show hospitality and a high regard for your guest than by giving him water to wash his feet.

Bethuel greeted Eliezer with great courtesy and Rivka and her mother set food before him. Eliezer, however, refused to eat.

"No," he said, "I cannot break bread with you or take food from your table until I tell you who I am and why I am here. Do I have your permission to speak ?"

"Speak, said Bethuel.

"I am the Chief Steward of the house of Abraham, your kinsman," began Eliezer portenously. "The Lord God has blessed my master, your kinsman, in every way. His flocks of sheep and goats are numberless. His herds of cattle are very great. Numerous manservants and maidservants run to do his bidding and he has considerable amounts of gold and silver. I know, because I am in charge of his household and I swear to you by the one true living God that I am speaking the truth."

Eliezer stopped and looked at his audience. Lavan's eyes were glistening and Bethuel was stroking his beard.

"But my master's greatest treasure," Eliezer went on, "is his only son, Yitzchak. The boy is tall and handsome. His face and form are the perfection of manly beauty. He has a merry disposition and a kind heart. He is beloved and popular in the tribe of Abraham and will surely succeed to the tribal chieftanship when, in good time and as God wills it, his father passes away."

Eliezer looked at Rivka. Her eyes were shining.

"I have been sent here," said Eliezer, "To find a bride for Yitzchak."

Chapter XV

When Eliezer finished speaking there was complete silnce. Bethuel, the master of the house maintained a grave courteous silence. Lavan cleared his throat, but decided not to speak—yet. Let the other side show its hand completely, was his motto, then make your carefully considered reply.

The women, of course, sat in the background and kept silent. Women did not interfere in men's affairs. Rivka sighed deeply and put her hand into her mother's hand. Her mother patted Rivka's hand comfortingly and squeezed slightly—transmitting hope and trust to her daughter.

Eliezer noted the reactions to his words. It was going well. He smiled inside but his face showed no expression as he said, "Now that I have told you who I am and why I am here, I shall—with your kind permission — partake of the food and drink which you have so hospitably placed before me."

When he had finished eating and drinking, Eliezer curteously thanked his host and protested: no, he could not touch another morsel of food or drink another drop of wine. He called out to his men, who came in carrying the packs and placed them in front of him.

Slowly, using every dramatic device he knew, Eliezer opened the packs and spread out their contents before him. Valuable ornaments and utensils of the finest gold and silver. Boxes of ebony and ivory, filled with precious gems. Garments of expensive fabrics, exquisitely made and cleverly fashioned.

"These are Abraham's gifts to his kinsmen," said Eliezer.

Bethuel and his family watched fascinatedly.

However, they were under no illusions. This fortune spread before their eyes was not a gift. It was the bridal price.

The bridal price — or "mohar" — as it is known to this very day in the Middle East, is a custom whereby the young man "buys" the bride from her father. The more beautiful and desirable the girl is, the higher her price.

Of course, in modern Israel, this custom is falling into disuse. But it took the young men and women of families coming from Oriental countries many domestic battles to convince the fathers that they were not entitled to collect a "bridal price" for their daughters.

That, however, was to be in the future. Rivka, her eyes shining, was very flattered at the high price her as yet unseen bridegroom was offering for her, especially if he was as handsome as Eliezer said. In the meantime, Eliezer was speaking.

"My master, Abraham, does not want his son to marry a Canaanite girl. He wishes his daughter-in-law to come from a family that worships the one, true living God. My master commanded me to find a bride for his son. When I protested that I was unworthy of performing so important a task, he said that God Himself would guide me and that angels of God would show me the way.

"And so it was, good people. Oh, the wonders my unworthy eyes have seen. The Lord God filled the heavens before me with signs and portents. Bands of angels marched before me all the way, singing. When I came to your city, an archangel stood at my shoulder—invisible to all but me, of course— and he pointed his hand at your daughter, Rivka, and he said to me that this is the girl that God wants for Yitzchak's bride.

"Yitzchak is the son of Abraham. God loves Abraham, said the archangel to me, and God will be very angry with anyone who denies God's plans for his favorite's son. Woe will be unto him, the archangel said, and fire and smoke issued forth from his mouth as he spoke."

Lavan nodded his head slightly and Bethuel answered Eliezer, "I am a humble God-fearing man. If this is what the Lord of heaven and earth wants, I cannot deny Him. Take my daughter, Rivka, to be the bride of Yitzchak, son of my kinsman, Abraham. Blessed be the name of the Lord."

"Rivka will be ready to travel in about ten days," the mother spoke up courageously. "There are dresses to be made and farewell feasts to be given."

"God will stand for no delay," said Eliezer. "We will start for Beer Sheba tomorrow morning."

Eliezer stood adamant against all protests and

he had his way. Early the next morning, Rivka and her chosen handmaidens mounted the camels and, amid a flurry of farewells and tears and good wishes for her happiness, away they went.

All the way home, Eliezer kept worrying that something might still go wrong with his mission, that Abraham might not be satisfied with his choice, that Yitzchak would be displeased with his bride. Rivka, however — like all happy brides — made the journey in a pleasurable glow of anticipation.

Eliezer need not have worried. Abraham approved of his choice. As for Yitzchak, he fell in love with Rivka at first sight. One look at her beautiful face and the Canaanite girl's languishing glances were forgotten. Rivka's voice as she said, "Greetings, my cousin," was music that went straight to his sorely troubled heart and healed the hurt there.

Rivka, for her part, was enchanted with Yitzchak. He was everything Eliezer had said — and more. A girl couldn't ask for a handsomer bridegroom.

Yitzchak gave Rivka the dress embroidered in silver and gold and told her the story.

"My mother said that my bride would wear it," he said. "Will you year it — wear it at our wedding?"

The tears glistened in Rivka's eyes and she nodded, not trusting her voice. Yitzchak was touched.

"How sweet she is," he thought, "how tenderhearted."

Aloud he said, "Dear cousin, I love you. I swear to you that I shall do everything in my power to make you happy."

From beneath her lashes she looked up at him and answered, "My heart was yours from the moment I saw you. I shall try to be a good wife to you."

They stood, that evening, with bowed heads before Abraham as he pronunced them man and wife. In the feasting, the singing and the dancing that followed, Yitzchak's merry laugh rang out as it used to and everyone said that the chieftan's son was quite himself again.

Shortly thereafter, Peleg came to Yitzchak and said, "Little chief, I am getting married and we should like you to bless our union."

Yitzchak smiled. To Peleg and Naor he would always be 'Little Chief," even if they all lived as long as the famous Methuselah. They simply could not bring themselves to call him by any other name.

"Whom are you marrying, Peleg?" he asked.

"Reumah," answered Peleg matter-of-factly.

"Reumah?" Yitzchak was amazed. "But I thought she favored Naor."

"It isn't the talkers who carry off the prizes," said Peleg modestly.

"I shall be very glad to bless your union," said Yitzchak. "But what does Naor say to all this ?"

"Better ask him," said Peleg as he took his departure. "Here he comes, poor fellow."

"Good morning, little chief," boomed Naor, "You look wonderfully well. Marriage agrees with a man, doesn't it?"

"Well, it agrees with me," said Yitzchak.

"Little chief," said Naor abruptly, "I want to get married and we should like you to bless our union."

Yitzchak's eyebrows rose. If that flirt Reumah had promised to marry both of them—and she was perfectly capable of it, the little jade—then he intended to spank her personally.

"I'd be glad to bless your union, Naor," said Yitzchak cautiously. "Whom are you going to marry?"

"Kedumah," said Naor. "Do you know her?"

"Of course," said Yitzchak in relief. "A fine girl."

Well, God be praised, there wasn't going to be any trouble, after all. To have Peleg and Naor fighting over a girl would have disrupted the life of the tribe for months. Still, Yitzchak could not control his curiosity.

"Naor," he said finally, "I thought you were fond of Reumah."

"I am fond of her," laughed Naor. "She's a girl of spirit and character. That kind is fine for courting. But for marrying—Lord, no! For marrying, I'll take a soft, easy-going woman that'll give me a little comfort in my home."

Yitzchak smiled. He had both kinds in one woman, his beloved Rivka. Still smiling, he turned homeward.

Chapter XVI

One morning, a young man of the tribe came running to Yitzchak. His father wanted to see him immediately. Yitzchak hastened to his father's house. He found Abraham lying in his bed.

How thin and frail his father seemed to Yitzchak's anxious eyes ! The old man's eyes were bright with fever, but his head was clear. When he spoke his voice was weak, but it had the old ring of command in it.

"Yitzchak, my son, I am an old man and my soul

is hesitating but for a moment before it leaves my body. Don't try to interrupt me. Listen carefully to what I tell you now."

Abraham fought for a moment for the breath with which to continue speaking—and won.

"Everything that I have I leave to you, my son. Lead the trible wisely. I leave my people in your hands with confidence. You are ready for leadership. Don't just keep repeating the things I have done. When things change, change with them. Use your own judgement. Listen to everyone's counsel, then make your own decision.

"Only in one thing you must never change." The old man's eyes grew stern. "Don't ever abandon the one true God. Walk in His ways forever and He will bless you and your children forever. As I bless you now, my son—my dear son."

Yitzchak, on his knees at his father's bedside, bowed his head and Abraham put his hand upon it in blessing. When he raised his tear-filled eyes, he was surprised to see that Abraham was smiling.

In a voice that was a mere thread of a whisper Abraham said, "Yitzchak, do you want to know what the happiest moment of my life was ? It was when the angel of the Lord said that I didn't have to sacrifice you!"

He leaned his head back, eyes closed, resting.

One moment he was breathing and the next moment he was not. The change from life to death went by almost unnoticed.

Yitzchak rose to his feet. Abraham, the leader of the tribe, was dead. Never again would he appear to take the weight of command from his son's shoulders so that he could weep and mourn his loss. Never again could Yitzchak afford to let himself weep. He must lead the tribe. He felt very lonely.

Yitzchak went to the door and spoke to the two young men on guard.

"My father is dead," said Yitzchak in a level voice, "You see to it that his body is prepared for burial. You summon the tribal council."

He walked slowly to the meeting place of the tribal council. When the elders of the tribe had all assembled, he addressed them.

"Respected elders of the tribe of Abraham, my father is dead. His last wish was that I take over the leadership of the tribe. Dearly as I loved my father and obedient as I was to his every wish, I will not take the leadership of the tribe upon myself if one of you, respected elders objects. If one of you thinks he, or someone else, is a better leader of the tribe than I am, then I am willing to give up my place and my heritage to him. The tribe of Abraham must be united behind the man who leads it. Does anyone wish to speak?"

There was a low murmur from the assembled elders which increased in volume until the oldest among them rose to speak.

"Yitzchak, son of Abraham," he said, "lead us. We trusted and followed your father. We shall trust and follow you. All of us, here and now, swear loyalty to you before the one true living God, who chose your father to make Him known to the peoples of the world."

"So be it," Yitzchak. 'Now my first sad duty is to bury my father. It is my decision that he is to be buried next to his beloved wife, Sarah, in the tomb he bought for her in the field called Machpelah, before Mamre in the City of Hebron."

So once again Yitzchak travelled along the caravan route to Hebron, this time in a funeral cortege behind the body of his father. He was followed by a number of the kinsmen he had chosen to accompany him and share his sad task.

Once the last rites were over and his father had been placed in his final resting place, Yitzchak hurried back to Beer Sheba. It was not good for the leader to be too long absent from his tribe.

Besides, he was anxious to get back to his beloved wife, Rivka. Only in the comfort of her arms could he allow himself the luxury of weeping. And Rivka would soothe him, as his mother had done when he was a child and had come crying to her.

Only with Rivka could he let himself go and be as a little child. To everyone else he was the leader of the tribe, wise and strong and fearless. Only Rivka knew what was in his heart and she did not know everything that he held there. There was one secret that he kept from everyone, even from his beloved wife.

There was one hunger even she could not satisfy, one desire that even she could not fulfill : the hunger to hear God's voice, the burning desire to speak with God as his father, Abraham, had.

The weeks went by, however, and Yitzchak felt no call. He walked night after night in the desert beneath the glittering stars; but he heard no Voice, he felt no Presence.

As the weeks became months, Yitzchak despaired. Rivka felt something was wrong, but he did not answer her questions. This was one thing he could not speak of — to anyone.

On the cold nighttime sand of the desert, he prostrated himself and prayed.

"God of Abraham, I beg you, speak to me as You did to my father. Let me hear Your voice. Tell me what to do. If I am to lead Your people, guide me. Tell me whether I am doing right or wrong.

"Lord God, I was willing to give up my life for You when I was only a boy. I am ready to do so now. I shall devote my life to leading Your people in Your ways. Only speak one word to me !"

There was no sound. There was no sign.

"Lord God, am I so unworthy?"

Silence.

Chapter XVII

There was great rejoicing when Rivka presented Yitzchak with twins, both boys. The older was a big, bouncing lad with fiery red hair. He was named Esau. The younger boy was dark and delicate. He was named Jacob.

Twice, Yitzchak was guest of honor in Peleg's house in celebration of Peleg's becoming a father — girls, both times. Twice, Yitzchak was guest of honor at Naor's house in celebration of the birth of his children, both boys.

Naor had a new subject to tease Peleg about. He would drawl, "Ye-e-es, the real men of this tribe are fathering sons. Look at the Little Chief, twin

He was deeply asleep in a moment.

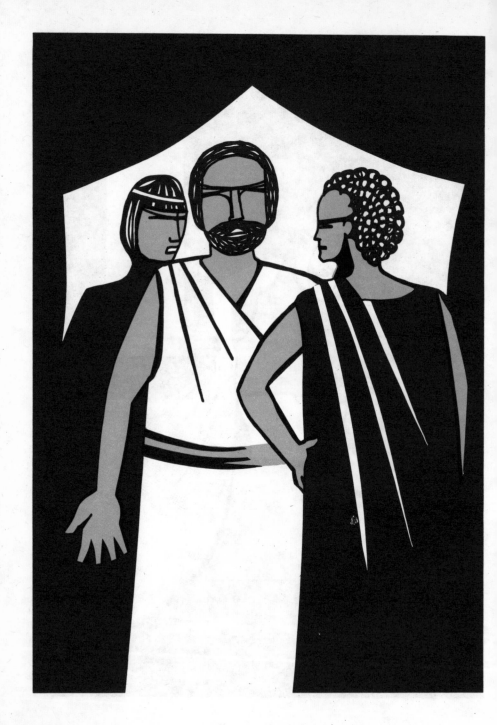

"You and your people will have to leave our land."

boys. And me — two boys. The tribe needs warriors and we are doing our duty to the tribe. Some of us don't seem to realize the tribe's need for warriors, so they permit themselves the luxury of fathering girls."

As Peleg kept sullenly silent, Yitzchak answered, "Don't talk nonsense, Naor. The tribe needs girls, too. Our boys can't marry Canaanite girls."

"You're right, Little Chief," said Naor reflectively, "you're right. Well, if Peleg won't ask too high a bridal price, I'll buy his girls for my boys."

Goaded beyond endurance, Peleg burst forth, "I'd throw my daughters to jackals and hyenas to be torn to pieces before I'd let them marry your whelps." And he stamped off, in a towering rage. Naor looked after him sorrowfully.

"Trouble with Peleg," he said mock-mournfully, "is that he never could take a joke."

One of Yitzchak's duties as head of the tribe was to preside at the regular sacrifice made to the Lord. It was a duty he performed with great reluctance. He could never approach the altar with the sacrificial knife in his hand, chanting the sacrificial prayer, without remembering himself as he had lain bound and helpless on the altar. His heart still remembered the fear of death, the terror of the approaching knife.

It was worse when a lamb was being sacrificed. Yitzchak had never gotten over his boyhood love of lambs. The lamb would lie bound upon the altar, bleating and rolling its eyes in terror and those eyes would fix themselves upon Yitzchak as he approached the altar with the knife. The eyes seemed to say to Yitzchak, "Why are you killing me? Why? I thought you were my friend."

"Don't tell me the animals don't know what's happening," Yitzchak would think. "They may not understand, but they sense. They feel! They know! It makes me feel like a murderer."

Thus it was, when a number of rainless years coming one after the other caused a famine in the land, Yitzchak felt guilty. Perhaps it was because he had performed the sacrifices with an unwilling heart. He did not know how the Lord felt about it. The Lord had never spoken to him.

However, he had no time to brood about it. Decisions had to be made and, having been made, they had to be carried out. There was too much to be done. There was just no time to sit and worry.

One thing was clear to Yitzchak. The tribe could not stay on in Beer Sheba under these conditions. They would starve to death. This was the worst famine that the land had known since the time of Abraham. Abraham, himself, had said to him,

"When conditions change, change with them. Don't just keep repeating the same things I used to do."

Yitzchak decided that the tribe must take to the tents again and become nomads once more. He would lead them into the land of Egypt, that fertile country where bread was never scarce. It was a great wrench to leave the city his father had founded, but starvation could not be argued with. Besides, Yitzchak swore in his heart that he would one day lead the tribe back to the city and that Beer Sheba would yet flourish in the desert.

On the way to Egypt, Yitzchak decided to visit Abimelech, the Philistine king who had made a treaty with his father, in those far-off days when Abraham had first tried to settle in Beer Sheba. Abimelech received him cordially and welcomed him warmly, assuring him that he could stay in the Valley of Gerar for as long as he liked.

Yitzchak had to smile to himself as he looked at Abimelech and at his Commander of the Army, Phicol. Were these the two giants with the booming voices that had struck terror in the heart of the child Yitzchak as he watched them arguing with his father? True, they were doughty old warriors, but they were merely old men and Yitzchak did not fear them.

That evening, as Yitzchak sat before his tent, it

suddenly hit him like a blow between the eyes. God was calling to him. Fear and joy struggled for mastery in his heart as he walked, like an automaton, out into the desert to answer the call of his God—as his father, Abraham, had before him.

He seemed to know where to go, he did not know how. He felt when to stop, he did not know why. Suddenly, he felt the pain and ecstasy of the Presence of God. His heart choking him, he flung himself down upon the sand and hid his eyes from the unendurable glory. He drew his robe up to cover his head, but to no avail.

He saw God—not with his eyes. He heard God's voice—not with his ears. In fear and trembling, in awe-struck joy, his soul took wing and Yitzchak, for the first time in his life, listened to his God's command.

"Yitzchak, son of Abraham, do not be afraid. I am the God of your father. Listen to my command and obey my voice, as your father did before you.

"Do not go down into Egypt. Stay in this land. I will be with you and I will bless you.

"I swore to your father that this land would belong to his people. I shall keep my oath.

"I swore to your father that his people would be as countless as the stars of the sky. I shall keep my oath.

"I swore to your father that, in your people, all the

114

nations of the world would be blessed. I shall keep my oath.

"Keep faith with Me and I shall keep faith with you, Yitzchak, son of Abraham."

The Voice ceased and God was gone.

For a long time, Yitzchak lay upon the cold, desert sand. He was dazed, dazzled and deafened by the sight and sound of glory.

Finally, he raised his tear-stained eyes to heaven and said huskily, "I shall keep the faith, my Lord, I shall keep the faith."

Yitzchak rose from the sand and reeled dizzily. He sank to his knees and stayed there until the dizziness had left him, then rose once more and walked homeward on unsteady feet.

Rivka rose in concern as he entered the tent.

"My lord," she cried, "what is it? What has happened?"

"Glory," he whispered, "Glory, glory, glory! My eyes have looked on the glory of God. My ears have heard His voice. Glory, glory, glory !"

Like one drunk with too much wine, he fell down upon the bed and was deeply asleep in a moment.

Rivka went to see to the twins. After she had covered them, she returned and covered her sleeping husband. She looked down at him for a long time, deep in troubled thought.

She knew now how Sarah must have felt. It was an awesome thing to be married to a man who spoke with God.

Chapter XVIII

Yitzchak rose the next morning like a man reborn, recreated. The tension that the cares and worries of leadership had built up inside him seemed to slip away and his merry laugh rang out all morning long. He wolfed down an enormous breakfast, flirted clownishly with Rivka until she had to laughingly slap him away, and played for hours with the twins. He roughhoused with Esau and played riddle games with Jacob.

He then went to pay a courtesy call on King Abimelech and so charmed the old king that he himself brought up the subject of Yitchak's staying on—a subject that Yitzchak had intended to introduce.

"Stay with us, Yitzchak, dear son of my friend, Abraham," said Abimelech, "Stay with us and don't make the long trek to Egypt. We've plenty of room. You can have the Valley of Gerar, you and your people. You're welcome to stay as long as you like. I'll send out commands that anyone who hurts or offends you or your family will feel our royal wrath. Come on, my dear boy, say you'll stay !"

Yitzchak let himself be persuaded and finally left King Abimelech in a good humor, feeling very pleased with himself that he had won his point and had persuaded Yitzchak to stay on with him.

Yitzchak's head buzzed with plans. He sent Eliezer off on another flying camel trip to Lavan to make a deal for seed wheat. The tribe was busy all spring long, settling in, re-digging old wells that had been stopped up and digging new ones.

Everyone pitched in and young and old worked like beavers, ploughing and harrowing, lugging stones aside and preparing the fertile acres of the Gerar Valley for the spring planting. When Peleg complained that this was no work for warriors, Naor had the entire tribe laughing and repeating his latest witticism that Peleg has finally found a use for his spear and was a much better ploughman than spearman — and wasn't it lucky that the tribe had a champion wrestler who could wrestle with such large stones!

Eliezer arrived in time, with his camels loaded high with sacks of seed. Again, the whole tribe pitched in and the sowing was completed in a week. Morale was high and everyone felt purposeful and dedicated and kept working though hot, tired, and sweaty. The land saw the same phenomenon again four thousand years later, when young descendants of Abraham began building their kibbutzim in Israel reborn. But that is — if not another story, then a later chapter of the same one.

The long, hot summer was spent in weeding and irrigating the sprouting wheat. In digging for a well, some of the tribesmen had discovered an underground stream, so there was no lack of water. The idea of irrigating crops seemed to spring forth in Yitzchak's mind. Before that, and for centuries after, men depended on the rain.

Autumn went by in a fury of harvesting, threshing, and winnowing. The crop was safely stored before the winter rains came. And what a crop! No one had heard of anything like it—a hundred fold, if the old legend is reliable. That means that, for every grain planted, one hundrd grains were harvested. Modern agricultural methods have improved on that record but, for that time, it was phenomenal.

The tribe prospered and increased. With unlimited water and plentiful fodder, the flocks of sheep and goats, the herds of cattle belonging to the tribe grew great indeed. The tribe was blessed by prosperity—and cursed by it.

Prosperity brings envy. The Philistines of the surrounding country had been sorry for the poor, hungry refugees from famine who had come into their lands just a few years ago. Now that the refugees had become rich—well, that was another story.

The envious Philistines did not take into consideration the thoughtful planning and the hard work that had gone into achieving prosperity. They, too, had plenty of land. They, too, had water. They could have done the same thing that Yitzchak's people had done. But it was easier to rob than to work— or so the Philistines thought!

As a first step, they tried to take away the wells and the source of the underground stream from the "defenceless" shepherds and farmers. They got the hock of their lives! In the twinkling of an eye, the shepherds and farmers dropped tools, picked up weapons and were fighting for their property with a ferocity that sent the would-be robbers scurrying.

Abimelech and Phicol came storming into Yitzchak's tent the next morning. Phicol's face was like a thundercloud, but Abimelech spoke more in sorrow than in anger.

"You and your people will have to leave our land, Yitzchak," the old king said. "You will be permitted to depart in peace but, before you go, I would like to make the same pact with you that I did with your father. I shall not make war upon you and will help you in case of need and you will do the same for me."

"We don't need them," growled Phicol.

"Don't contradict me," snapped Abimelech, "Are you too stupid to see that the mighty God that blessed Abraham stands at Yitzchak's side? I want that kind of God on my side in an emergency."

Yitzchak made a great feast for King Abimelech and his company and they swore peace and fealty between them. The next morning, the tribe took up their tents again and Yitzchak turned his face toward his beloved city, Beer Sheba.

Yitzchak's remaining years in the city that his father had founded were peaceful and happy ones. There were worries and problems, of course, but they were overcome by thoughtful planning and decisive action.

He watched his twin sons carefully. One of them would succeed him to the leadership of the tribe. By right, it should be the firstborn, Esau; but Yitzchak watched with some concern as Esau grew up to be a brutal, violent man—a hunter who loved killing for killing's sake.

Jacob, on the other hand, was a shy, sensitive boy, who reminded Yitzchak of his own youth. He grew up to be a quiet, thoughtful man—interested in the problems of farming and sheep raising and quite clever at finding new, better ways of doing things.

When Esau married a girl from the Hittite tribe, Yitzchak's mind was made up. Jacob must have the leadership of the tribe. However, Yitzchak had to be careful. He remembered the story of Cain and Abel. Esau, too, was a violent man and would not hesitate to kill his brother if he had the slightest reason for jealousy.

So, through the years, Yitzchak showed outright partiality for Esau. Rivka was indignant. She knew which was the better son. Esau was not bothered by his mother's opinion. As long as he had his father's favor, he felt that he had nothing to worry about.

Yitzchak grew old and infirm. His sight was dim and his limbs were feeble; but his brain was active and his wits were still sharp. He called his oldest son to him.

"Esau," he spoke as loudly as he could, "Esau, my beloved son, take your bow and go hunting. Bring me back some venison and I will eat it and bless you and pass the leadership on to you."

Esau departed with a great clattering of

weapons and hunting gear, Yitzchak leaned back and listened.

"Now," he thought, "now, Jacob, if you're as clever as I think you are, make your move. The next leader of the tribe will have to be bold, resourceful and intelligent. If you're the man for the job, my boy, now is the time to prove it."

Chapter XIX

Yitzchak did not have to wait very long. No sooner had Esau disappeared from sight, then he heard Rivka calling to Jacob and their whispering voices came floating in to him on the morning breeze.

"Not so loud, you two plotters," he chuckled to himself. "It's my eyes that are supposed to be dim My hearing's perfect."

He heard Jacob go off to the flock to bring back a kid. He heard the preparations and smelt the savory odors of cooking as Rivka cleverly blended the spices that would make goat's meat taste like venison.

The smell of cooking reminded him of that far-off day long ago when he had run up to his mother making breakfast and had bolted down the meal because he was impatient to start off on the journey with his father. Yitzchak subsided into the half-doze of the very old and gave himself over to memory.

He remembered the strange journey to Mount Moriah and the altar and the suffering face of his father as he stood with the sacrificial knife in his hand.

He remembered the glory of the angel and the incomparably greater glory of God. How happy he had been when the Lord had finally called him and spoken to him. The Lord had appeared to him again just before the return to Beer Sheba. Oh, blessed glory !

His friends and kinsmen passed one by one before his remembering eyes. Peleg and Naor — dear teachers, good companions, comrades-in-arms. He smiled as he remembered how he, as head of the tribe, had insisted that Naor's sons and Peleg's daughters were to be married. My, how those two rivals had blustered and spulttered! Then they had settled down and became doting grandfathers to a brood of grandchildren. They spoiled the little girls outrageously and trained the boys rigorously. Some of the tribe's best warriors came from that family.

He woke from his doze with a start. Someone

was standing in the entrance with a smoking bowl of savory meat in his hands. He peered short-sightedly at him and then, as he made out who it was, with difficulty suppressed a roar of rib-cracking laughter.

Good Lord, did they think he was completely blind? Jacob stood there across the room holding out the bowl. He was dressed in an old set of Esau's hunting clothes and he had wrapped his neck, chest and arms in goatskins in a crude imitation of Esau's hairy body.

That Rivka! She had put the boy up to this, of course. Yitzchak could sense her, just out of sight behind the doorway, listening.

"Dear wife," thought Yitzchak, "do you think my wits are completely addled, my brain gone feeble ?"

Look at that poor boy! He was hating every second of this deception. He was sure it would fail and that his father would curse him instead of bless him. You could see it in his face. But his mother had insisted on this charade and, because he loved his mother and could deny her nothing, he was going to go through with it to the bitter end.

That showed courage and determination. Having adopted a line of action, though against his better judgement, he was seeing it through. The boy did look funny, though. Yitzchak's voice quivered with mirth as he asked, "Who is it?"

Jacob kept his voice as low as possible as he answered, "Here is the venison you asked for, father."

"All right," thought Yitzchak, "we'll play out this charade for dear Rivka's sake. I would have preferred you to have made your bid for the leadership openly, my son, in your own name."

Aloud, he said, "Who are you?"

"I am Esau, your firstborn," said Jacob. "Here is the venison you asked for, my father."

"How did you find it so soon?"

"The Lord sent it to me, father."

"Quick-witted young scamp, aren't you?" thought Yitzchak, chuckling to himself.

"Is that really you, my son?" Yitzchak said aloud. "Come closer so that I may see for myself."

Jacob's face plainly showed that he realized the game was up, but he moved determinedly and resignedly forward until he stood before his father. Yitzchak ran his hand tentatively over the goatskin.

"The voice is Jacob's voice," he said, "But the hands are the hands of Esau. Bring me the venison, my son, that I may eat."

Jacob hurriedly set the dish in front of his father and brought him wine to drink. After he had eaten,

Yitzchak said to his son, "Come near to me and kiss me and I will bless you."

As his son kissed him, Yitzchak took the boy's face in his hands and looked him squarely in the eye. Yitzchak's lips twitched and finally relaxed in a humorous smile and he winked at his son.

Jacob, realizing that Yitzchak knew of his deception, flushed and bowed his head in shame. Yitzchak put his hands upon his son's head and blessed him and gave the leadership of the tribe over into his son's hands.

Jacob rose from his knees and left the room quickly, walking into his jubilant mother's arms.

Esau, of course, was furious when he learned of what had happened. In spite of all of Yitzchak's efforts to placate his older son, Esau stormed out of the room shouting, "I'll kill him! I'll kill him!"

"No, you won't kill him, my fine bully boy," mused Yitzchak, "Jacob will be too clever for you. He'll always be too clever for you."

Yitzchak was right. Esau never did manage to kill Jacob. And his descendants never managed to kill off the tribe of Jacob. Some always managed to escape and live on.

The End

"I'll kill him! I'll kill him!"